Autumn 2 Writing Assessment   Year 2

Facility CMIS
Class group: Year 2 (Thomas, J)

CLASS LIST

Surname	Forename				
Abdirahman	Adan Said	1A			
Abell	Liah	2C			
Ahmed	Sherly	1A			
BAINS	Ryan	2C			
BANFORD	Emma	1A			
BROWN	D'Andre	1A			
Cunningham	Unaysah	2C			
DAVIDSON	Jayden	2B			
DOVASTON	Stacey	1C			
Douthwaite	Summer	2C			
Emungu	Salva	W			
FATAWU	Fatimat Abdul	2C			
HENRY	Daniel	2C			
HINDS	Anton	1A			
HUSSAIN	Mariam	2C			
JAMES	Tyreke	W+			
Liang	Tonny	2C			
MAHMOOD	Halima	2C			
MHANGO	Peniel	1A			
MILLS	Dajean	1A			
POWELL	La'shantay	1A			
RUTHERFORD	Jordan	1C			
RUTHERFORD	Jayden	1A			
SAPPELTON	Kosheen	1B			
Sowe	Brian	1B			
WELLINGTON	Akeem	2C			
WIZZARD	Duaine	2C			

Surname	Forename	Class							
Abdirahman	Adan Said	Y2T	1						
Abell	Liah	Y2T	2						
Ahmed	Sherly	Y2T	3						
BAINS	Ryan	Y2T	4						
BANFORD	Emma	Y2T							
BROWN	D'Andre	Y2T	5						
Cunningham	Unaysah	Y2T	6						
DAVIDSON	Jayden	Y2T							
DOVASTON	Stacey	Y2T							
Emungu	Salva	Y2T							
FATAWU	Fatimat Abdul	Y2T	7						
HENRY	Daniel	Y2T	8						
HINDS	Anton	Y2T	9						
HUSSAIN	Mariam	Y2T	10						
JAMES	Tyreke	Y2T							
Liang	Tonny	Y2T	11						
MAHMOOD	Halima	Y2T	12						
MHANGO	Peniel	Y2T	13						
MILLS	Dajean	Y2T							
POWELL	La'shantay	Y2T	14						
RUTHERFORD	Jordan	Y2T							
RUTHERFORD	Jayden	Y2T	15						
SAPPELTON	Kosheen	Y2T							
Sowe	Brian	Y2T							
WELLINGTON	Akeem	Y2T	16						
WIZZARD	Duaine	Y2T	17						

Colleen Y2

Contents

Photocopy Masters

Introduction

The Abacus Model

The Abacus materials are designed and written to allow for a daily, structured mathematics lesson:

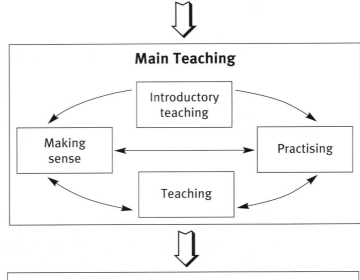

Mental Warm-up Activities
- Rehearsing previously-taught strategies
- Counting
- Number facts

Main Teaching

Introductory teaching

Making sense

Practising

Teaching

Plenaries
- Reinforcing key skills
- Addressing common difficulties
- Concluding with feedback or an activity

Each day's teaching begins with a whole class mental maths activity. These are presented in the **Mental Warm-up Activities** book.

The main part of the lesson is supported by the **Teacher Cards**:

- the front of each card gives support for whole class teaching for the first day of a topic
- the back of each card gives advice on further teaching for subsequent days and references to the practical activities included in this book. References to relevant **Workbook** pages and **Photocopy Masters** are also provided.

Each lesson is rounded-off with a plenary session. Guidance on key points to reiterate, common misconceptions to look out for, and whole class activities is included on the back of each Teacher Card.

Activity Book

The activities in this book are intended as follow-up to the introductory teaching. Each Unit of the programme is supported by a range of activities covering different styles, numbers of children, resources etc.

Each activity includes the following information:

- Appropriate number of children, e.g. pairs, 3-4 children, whole class.
- A list of relevant materials. Any 'specialist' resources, e.g. number grids, number tracks … are provided as Photocopy Masters at the back of the book. Number lines, number cards, place-value cards etc. are supplied separately in the **Resource Bank**.
- Level of difficulty, indicated by the following codes:

  ● basic work

  ●● for all children

  ●●● enrichment and extension.

- Learning points are also provided, drawing on the teaching objectives from the Teacher Card. These learning points will assist the teacher in directing the group and making informal assessments. They are also useful as key points to highlight in the plenary session – it may be beneficial to give the children some points to consider when setting up the activity. This will give them a clear focus for the outcome of the activity and any key points they might raise in the plenary session.

Whole class work

Following the initial teaching input, it is often a useful strategy to carry out some immediate consolidation, with the whole class or large group, working on an appropriate activity. Many of the units include a whole class activity specifically written to support this strategy. Such activities are indicated by the icon:

We suggest that following the initial teaching input for the whole class activity, the children are arranged in pairs or small groups, and work independently for a short period exploring or consolidating their learning. These activities will sometimes lead into the plenary session, where the topic can be rounded-off with a discussion about what the children have learned, any difficulties they encountered etc.

Classroom management

When working with groups it is important to have a manageable number of groups (about four is ideal). It may be appropriate for one or two of those groups to be working from a Workbook, Photocopy Master, or Textbook page. You should try to focus your attention on one or two groups, working intensively with them, directing, discussing, evaluating etc. The Abacus model assists management by ensuring that all the children are broadly working within the same topic, at the same time as providing differentiated work through the activities in this book and the Photocopy masters.

The activities are written with enough details covering resources and learning outcomes (as well as the description of the activities themselves) to allow any support staff to manage easily.

ACTIVITY 1

Whole class, in pairs

- *Counting to 100*
- *Matching the spoken numbers to card numbers*

Number cards (1 to 100) (PCMs 2 to 8), place-value cards (tens and units) (PCMs 10 to 12)

Give each pair six number cards. Shuffle each set of place-value cards and put them in two piles, face down. Choose a child to take a tens and units card from each pile. Ask him to read the card numbers, e.g. *Forty* and *Six*. Write these as an addition, i.e. '40 + 6 = 46'. Ask the class *Who has card 46?* If a pair has the card, they stand up. Start counting at 40. As you say each number *Forty, forty-one, forty-two ...*, the pairs with any of those numbers stand up. Stop at 49. Each pair standing up reads out their number(s). If they do so correctly, they give the card(s) to you. Repeat, choosing another child to take a tens and a units card. Continue sometimes counting on, sometimes counting back, until one pair has no cards left.

ACTIVITY 2

3 children

- *Counting to 100 from any number forwards and back*

Blank number tracks (1 to 10) (PCM 1), number cards (0 to 9) (PCM 2)

Shuffle the cards and lay them out on the table face down. The first child takes two cards and puts them next to each other to make a 2-digit number. The second child writes the number in the middle of one of the tracks. The third child writes the number before or after it. The first child then writes a number before or after the numbers written so far. They continue until the track has a line of ten consecutive numbers written on it. E.g. the first child picks cards to make the number 27. The second child writes 27, the third child writes 28, the first child writes 29, the second child writes 30, the third child writes 26 and so on. When that track is full of numbers, the children start again with a different child starting.

ACTIVITY 3

3 children

- *Counting to 20*
- *Matching the spoken number to the numeral*
- *Ordering the numbers 1 to 20*

Number cards (1 to 20) (PCMs 2, 3), blank number track (1 to 20) (PCM 1 photocopied twice)

Shuffle the cards and place them in a pile face down. The children take turns to reveal a card. They decide where on the number track the cards will go so that the numbers 1 to 20 will be in the correct order. The first child places a card on the track. The next child takes a card and does the same. Gradually, they build up the track. If a card is in the wrong place they discuss where it should be.

ACTIVITY 4

3 children

- *Counting to 100*
- *Sequencing any set of numbers to 100*

Number cards (50 to 100) (PCMs 5 to 8)

Shuffle the cards and deal four to each child. They have to try to collect four numbers that make a sequence, e.g. 54, 55, 56, 57. They collect cards by asking each other for a card, e.g. *Have you got thirty-six?* If the answer is, *No*, they take another card from the pile. If the answer is, *Yes*, the child who has it must hand it over. They play until one child has four sequential cards. Repeat.

ACTIVITY 5

- *Matching coins to amounts (up to 50p)*

Infant game 12: 'Rope Race', coins (1p, 10p), a dice, counters

(See instructions on the card.)

N2 Place-value

ACTIVITY 1
Whole class, in groups of
3 children

- *Recognising the number of tens and units in a 2-digit number*
Number cards (1 to 100) (PCMs 2 to 8) one set per group, interlocking cubes (loose and in towers of ten)/coins (1p, 10p)
The children shuffle the cards and place them face down in a pile. They take turns to reveal a card. Together they must match the card with the correct number of either cubes or coins. Choose groups to show their number and matching set of cubes or coins. Repeat.

ACTIVITY 2
4 children

- *Recognising the number of tens and units in a 2-digit number*
Number cards (1 to 100) (PCMs 2 to 8), a calculator, interlocking cubes (loose and in towers of ten), coins (1p, 10p)
The first child enters a 2-digit number on the calculator and shows it to the second and third child but not to the fourth child. The second child matches the number with 10p and 1p coins. The third child matches the number with interlocking cubes. The fourth child looks at the cubes and the coins and selects the matching number card. They check on the calculator. Does the card match? Repeat the activity, swapping roles.

ACTIVITY 3
4 children

- *Recognising the number of tens and units in a 2-digit number*
- *Ordering 2-digit numbers*
Place-value cards (tens and units) (PCMs 10 to 12), counters
Shuffle the cards and place them face down in two piles. Each child takes one tens and one units card and creates a 2-digit number. They take turns to say their number, and how many tens and units there are in the number. Ask the children to place the numbers in order. The children with the smallest and largest numbers take a counter each. Let them replace the cards and play again several times. Who collects the most counters?

ACTIVITY 4
3-4 children

- *Recognising the number of tens and units in a 2-digit number*
Number grid 2 (PCM 14), grid window (PCM 17), coins (1p, 10p)
One child places the window on the grid to outline a 2-digit number, e.g. 5 and 8 showing 58. He hides it from the other children and matches the number with coins, i.e. five 10p and eight 1p coins. He removes the window and then shows the coins to the other children. The other children take the grid and have to outline the same 2-digit number. Repeat, taking turns to outline numbers.

ACTIVITY 5
2-4 children

- *Recognising and reading numbers (up to 100)*
Infant game 13: 'Number Crunch', a coin, a counter each
(See instructions on the card.)

ACTIVITY 1
Whole class, in pairs

- *Adding pairs which total 10*
Three sets of number cards (0 to 10) (PCM 2)
Shuffle the cards and place them in a pile, face down. Each pair draws four circles. In each circle they write a different number between 0 and 10, inclusive. Choose a child to take a card from the pile. He reads out the number. Which number can you pair with this number to make ten? Any pair who has written the answer in one of their circles may cross it out. E.g. if the card number is 4, those who have written '6' in a circle can cross it out. The children play until one pair has crossed out all of their numbers.

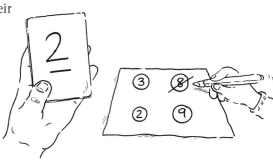

ACTIVITY 2
3 children

- *Adding pairs which total 10*
Number cards (0 to 10) (PCM 2), interlocking cubes
Shuffle the cards and lay them out on the table face down. One child reveals a card. He says the number which, when added to the card number, makes ten. He then takes that number of cubes. The next child has a turn. The children play until all the cards have been revealed. Who has the most cubes? Repeat.

ACTIVITY 3
3-4 children

- *Adding pairs which total 10*
Number grid 1 (PCM 13), number cards (1 to 10) (PCM 2), interlocking cubes
Shuffle the cards and place them in a pile face down. The children take turns to reveal a card. They place a cube on a number on the number grid, so that the card number and the grid number together total ten, and put the card at the bottom of the pile. The next child takes a card and does the same. The children continue until all the numbers on the grid have a cube.

ACTIVITY 4
3-4 children

- *Adding pairs which total 10*
Dice, interlocking cubes
The children take turns to throw the dice. They match the dice number with cubes in one colour. One child builds a tower with the cubes. Another child continues to build the tower up to ten using cubes of a different colour. The next child writes the matching addition, e.g. '4 + 6 = 10'. Repeat, swapping roles.

ACTIVITY 5
2-4 children

- *Adding pairs which total 10*
Infant game 14: 'Making ten', 18 wooden bricks
(See instructions on the card.)

ACTIVITY 1
Whole class, in pairs

- *Recognising coins*
- *Exchanging coins for equivalent amounts*

Coins (1p, 2p, 5p, 10p, 20p and one set Blu-tacked on the board)

Each pair takes a coin. They decide how many amounts can be made using their coin and any other coin in the set. Give them ten minutes to write down all the different amounts. *Which amounts can be made using a 1p with another coin? Which amounts using a 2p?* Ask the whole class for suggestions and write down the variations on the board.

ACTIVITY 2
3-4 children

- *Recognising coins*
- *Exchanging coins for equivalent amounts*

Coins (1p, 2p, 5p, 10p, 20p)

Place the coins on the table. The first child takes a 1p coin. The next child takes coins to the value of 2p, the next 3p (2p and 1p), and so on, in turn, up to 20p. The children must place the coins in rows on the table and select the fewest coins each time. Ask them to check each other's selections. Repeat the activity, with a different child taking the first coin.

ACTIVITY 3
4 children

- *Recognising coins*
- *Exchanging coins for equivalent amounts*

A collection of objects (labelled from 5p to 20p), coins (1p, 2p, 5p, 10p)

One child is the shopkeeper, the others are shoppers. Each shopper takes five of each coin. The shoppers take turns to buy something from the shop and hand over the fewest coins to match the value of the item. The shopkeeper collects the money and checks that the payments are correct. The children buy three items each. They return the items and the coins and repeat the activity with a different shopkeeper.

ACTIVITY 4
3-4 children

- *Recognising coins*
- *Exchanging coins for equivalent amounts*

Coins (1p to 20p), card for price labels (2p, 5p, 10p, 20p)

The children work together to decide how many 1p coins they need to place on each price label to match the price. When they have done this, they make a rubbing of the single coin which matches that price.

ACTIVITY 5
3-4 children

- *Recognising coins and their value*
- *Investigating adding different coins*

Coins (1p, 2p, 5p, 10p, 20p)

The children work together to decide how many different amounts they can make using two silver coins. When they have written them all, ask them to work out how many amounts they can make using two copper coins. Which amounts can be made with three silver coins?

N5 **Subtraction**

ACTIVITY 1
Whole class, in pairs

- *Subtracting a 1-digit number from a 'teen' number*
- *Subtracting by taking away*

Three sets of number cards (1 to 10) (PCM2)
Shuffle the cards and put them face down in a pile. Each pair draws four circles. In each one they write a different number between 10 and 19, inclusive. Choose a child to take a card from the pile. He reads out the number, e.g. *One.*
Write the number on the board, then write a subtraction taking away his number, e.g. '12 – 1 = '. (Create a subtraction which does NOT involve crossing the ten.) The children must complete the subtraction. If the answer is in one of their circles, they may cross it out. Continue until one pair has crossed out all their numbers.

ACTIVITY 2
Pairs

- *Subtracting ten from a 'teen' number*
- *Subtracting by taking away*

Number cards (10 to 19) (PCMs 2, 3), number grid 1 (PCM 13 – enlarged to A3)
Shuffle the cards and lay them out on the table face down. One child takes a card and turns it over. He reads the number. The other child works out the answer if **ten** is subtracted from the card number. He then places the card on that number on the grid. E.g. card 14, 14 take away 10 is 4, place the card on the 4 on the grid. Ask the children to write the subtraction to match: '14 – 10 = 4'. Repeat until all the cards have been turned over.

ACTIVITY 3
3-4 children

- *Subtracting by taking away (from numbers up to 10)*

Number grid 1 (PCM 13)
One child chooses two adjacent numbers on the grid. He subtracts the smaller from the larger and writes down the answer. The other children have to guess which two numbers he chose. When they have guessed, they all write down the subtraction, for example, '4 – 2 = 2'. Repeat with another child choosing the two adjacent numbers.

ACTIVITY 4
3-4 children

- *Subtracting by taking away*

Number cards (1 to 20) (PCMs 2, 3), calculators, counters
Shuffle the cards and place them face down in a pile. The children each enter a number on their calculators between 30 and 50. They each take a card and complete a subtraction on their calculator to give an answer to match the card. Any player who matches the card correctly collects a counter. Encourage the children to help each other. Can they collect five counters each?

ACTIVITY 1
Whole class, in pairs

- *Counting in tens from any 1-digit number*
- *Adding ten*

Large number grid (1 to 100) (PCM 19), a card or plastic spider, Blu-tack
Each pair draws four circles and writes a different 2-digit number in each. Choose a number on the top row of the grid and place the spider on it. Encourage the children to count in unison down that column. If any pair has written one of the numbers called out, they cross out that circle. Place the spider on another starting number at the top and count down again. Continue until a pair has crossed out all their circles.

ACTIVITY 2
3-4 children

- *Adding ten*

Number grid (1 to 100) (PCM 19), number cards (1 to 10) (PCM 2), interlocking cubes, a card or plastic spider
Shuffle the cards and place them in a pile face down. One child chooses a card and says the number. He places the spider on the grid, on the matching number. The children take turns to move the spider down one space and say the number. The child who moves the spider off the grid at the bottom can take a cube. Repeat, with a different child taking a card and placing the spider on the grid. They continue until all the cards have gone.

ACTIVITY 3
3 children

- *Adding to total up to 100*

Number cards (50 to 100) (PCMs 5 to 8), calculators, counters
Shuffle the cards and place them face down in a pile. The children each enter a number on their calculator between 30 and 50. They each take a card and take turns to complete an addition on the calculator to give an answer to match the card. Any player who matches the card correctly collects a counter. Encourage the children to help each other. Can they collect five counters each?

ACTIVITY 4
3 children

- *Adding to total up to 25*

Number cards (1 to 10, 12 to 25) (PCMs 2 to 4), coins (1p, 10p), a calculator
Shuffle the cards (1 to 10) and place them in a pile face down. The first child turns over the top card. The second child chooses an amount, between 11 and 15, and matches it with coins. They add this amount to the card number and find the card (from the 12 to 25 set) which matches the answer. They check their answer on the calculator and continue, sharing the roles.

ACTIVITY 5
3 children

- *Seeing differences of 11 in pairs of numbers*

Number cards (1 to 100) (PCMs 2 to 8)
The cards are spread out face up on the table. The children work together to take two cards and make a pair of numbers for which one number is 11 more than the other, e.g. 34 and 45. They record each pair. How many pairs can they make?

ACTIVITY 6
2-4 children

- *Adding 11 or 12 to total up to 70*

Infant game 15: 'Number lines', number cards (0 to 58) (PCMs 2 to 6), counters (one colour per player)
(See instructions on the card.)

N7 Numbers to 100

ACTIVITY 1
Whole class, in pairs

• *Recognising odd and even numbers (up to 100)*
A dice, a coin
Each pair draws five circles and writes a different 2-digit number, between 10 and 70, in each. Throw a dice – this is the tens digit. Write it on the board. Flip a coin – heads is even, tails is odd. The children are looking for, e.g. an even number in the thirties (the dice throw was 3, the coin landed 'heads'). Any pair who has a number which fits that description can cross it out. Repeat. The first pair to cross out all their circles wins.

ACTIVITY 2
3-4 children

• *Recognising even numbers (up to 20)*
Number cards (1 to 20) (PCMs 2, 3), interlocking cubes
The children lay out the number cards in multiples of 2, in order, up to 20. They build a tower to match each one. They divide the towers into two and leave them on the cards. What do they notice?

ACTIVITY 3
3 children

• *Recognising odd and even numbers (up to 50)*
Number cards (1 to 50) (PCMs 2 to 5), interlocking cubes
The children lay out the even numbers in order up to 50. They lay out the odd numbers in a separate line. They choose a number each and build a tower of cubes to match. They decide whether their tower can be divided into two equal towers, tell the others and then show that they are correct. E.g. they build a tower to match 34, they say it **can** be divided, they then try to divide it into two towers to create 17 cubes in each. They choose another number each and repeat.

ACTIVITY 4
4-5 children

• *Recognising odd and even numbers (up to 50)*
Number cards (1 to 50) (PCMs 2 to 5)
Shuffle the cards and deal seven to each child. Place the remainder face down in a pile. The children take turns to reveal the top card. If it is odd, they place it on a discard pile. If it is even, they swap it for one of the odd cards in their hand. The winner is the first child to collect seven even numbers.

ACTIVITY 5
3 children

• *Adding two numbers to give an even or odd total*
Number grid 1 (PCM 13), grid window (PCM 17)
The children place the window horizontally or vertically so that it reveals two numbers on the grid. They investigate different positions for the window where the total of the two numbers is even. They write down all the different combinations they can find. Repeat the activity, looking for two numbers which have an odd total.

ACTIVITY 6
3 children

• *Adding two numbers to give an even or odd total*
A set of dominoes
The children first sort the dominoes into two sets, those with an odd total of spots, and those with an even total of spots. They count the number of dominoes in each set. How many dominoes in the odd set have at least one side that is odd? How many dominoes in the even set have at least one side that is even? Discuss the patterns that emerge.

ACTIVITY 7
2 pairs

• *Recognising odd and even 2-digit numbers*
Infant Game 16: 'Odd fish, even fish', number cards (11 to 42) (PCMs 3 to 5), counters
(See instructions on the card.)

ACTIVITY 1
Whole class, in pairs

• *Reasoning about number and organising ideas*
Two dice per pair
Each pair throws two dice and subtracts the smaller number from the larger one. They write down their answer. *Is there an answer which is larger than 5?* Draw a block graph on the board with the numbers 0 to 5 written along the bottom. *Who has an answer of 0?* For each pair with the answer 0, colour a square above the 0. Do the same for each number. Repeat the throws several times and discuss the final block graph with the children.

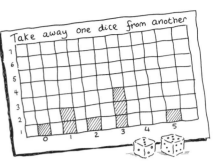

ACTIVITY 2
3-4 children

• *Reasoning about number and organising ideas*
A set of dominoes
Using four dominoes, the children lay out square outlines, matching the halves at the corners. They total up each square, adding all the spots, then draw them on paper and write the total number of spots, for each domino square, in the middle. They should make four or five different squares and compare the totals. What do they notice about all the totals? (They are all even.) Can they make a square with a very low total? Can they make a square with a high total? Discuss the patterns with the children. Extend by making bigger squares with six or eight dominoes.

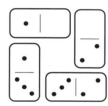

ACTIVITY 3
3 children

• *Reasoning about number and organising ideas*
Number cards (1 to 20) (PCMs 2, 3), two dice, interlocking cubes
Lay out the cards in order (1 to 20). The children throw two dice and add the numbers thrown. They put a cube on the card with that number and repeat. After they have thrown the dice 30 times, look at the cards they have used. Which cards have not been used? Which cards have lots of cubes? Which have only a few? Discuss the results.

ACTIVITY 4
3-4 children

• *Reasoning about number and organising ideas*
Number cards (1 to 9) (PCM 2)
Spread out the cards face up. The children have to find as many different totals as they can using three cards. How will they know they have found them all?

ACTIVITY 5
3-4 children

• *Reasoning about number and organising ideas*
• *Constructing and interpreting a block graph*
A dice (1 to 6), a dice (0,0,0,6,6,6)
Throw the two dice 30 times and construct a block graph to show how many times each total (1 to 12) was thrown. How does it compare with the block graph constructed on the Teacher Card?

ACTIVITY 1
Whole class, then in groups of
3 children

• *Recognising numbers which lie between two 2-digit numbers*
Number cards (10 to 35) (PCMs 2 to 4), number grid (1 to 100) (PCM 19)
Spread out the cards face down on the table. The children take turns to reveal two cards, then say all the numbers that are between the two card numbers. They check using the grid. If correct the two cards are kept. Otherwise the cards are replaced face down. The children continue until all the cards have been taken. Who has the most pairs? (For the whole class activity, group the children in two teams.)

ACTIVITY 2
4 children

• *Recognising all the numbers which lie between two 2-digit numbers*
Number cards (51 to 80) (PCMs 5 to 7), number grid (1 to 100) (PCM 19), interlocking cubes
Shuffle the cards and place them face down in a pile. The children take turns to reveal two cards, then say all the numbers between the two. The others check using the number grid. For each correct 'between' number they collect a cube. E.g. the child reveals 53 and 67 and says, *fifty-four, fifty-five ... sixty-six* – they collect 13 cubes. The winner is the first child to collect 40 cubes or more.

ACTIVITY 3
4 children

• *Recognising numbers which lie between two 2-digit numbers*
• *Recognising the place-value of digits in a 2-digit number*
Place-value cards (tens and units) (PCMs 10 to 12)
Shuffle the cards and place them face down in two piles (tens and units). Each child takes one tens card and one units card and creates a 2-digit number with them. The children take turns to say their number, and how many tens and units it has. They place the numbers in order. Each child then writes two numbers which lie between each pair of adjacent numbers. Ask the children to check each other's numbers.

ACTIVITY 4
3-4 children

• *Recognising numbers which lie between two 2-digit numbers*
• *Recognising the place-value of digits in a 2-digit number*
Number cards (10 to 50) (PCMs 2 to 5), number grid (1 to 100) (PCM 19), counters, coins (1p, 10p)
Shuffle the cards and place them face down in a pile. Ask the children to turn over the first two cards and place a counter on each of those numbers on the grid. The children take one new card each. Any child whose number lies between the two counter numbers, collects a matching amount of money in 10p and 1p coins. They continue until all the cards have been taken or until one child collects more than £1.

ACTIVITY 1
Whole class, in pairs

- *Using knowledge of addition pairs to 10*
- *Adding pairs of numbers (to total up to 20)*

Each pair draws five circles on a piece of paper and writes a number between 10 and 20 in each. Write an addition on the board using numbers up to 10, e.g. '4 + 8'. *Which number is larger? How many more do we need to make 10? We are adding eight and four. Eight needs two more to make* **ten** *and another two more makes twelve; eight and two and two is twelve. Who has that number in one of their circles?* Those who have cross it out. Continue until one pair has crossed out all their circles.

ACTIVITY 2
3 children

- *Adding pairs of numbers*

A set of dominoes

The children lay out the dominoes face down. The children take turns to choose two dominoes. They keep their dominoes hidden and write down the total number of spots on each, e.g. one domino has three spots and five spots (making eight), the other has two spots and one spot (making three). They show the other children their two numbers and they have to add them together and agree a total, i.e. eleven. They say the total and write it down as an addition, e.g. '8 + 3 = 11'. The first child then reveals the dominoes and they count all the spots. Were they correct? If so, the two other children take one each of the dominoes. Another child takes two new dominoes, keeping them hidden, and they play again. They continue until all the dominoes have been used.

ACTIVITY 3
3 children

- *Adding pairs of numbers to make 10 and 11*

Two sets of number cards (0 to 10) (PCM 2), interlocking cubes

The children spread out the cards face up. They put the cards into matching pairs to make ten. One child chooses a pair and writes an addition to make **11**, e.g. they choose 4 and 6 and write '4 + 7 = 11'. The children can match the addition with cubes in three colours to help (e.g. 4 red, 6 green, and 1 yellow), if necessary. Repeat for another pair of cards.

ACTIVITY 4
3-4 children

- *Adding a 1-digit number to a 2-digit number*
- *Recognising multiples of ten*

Number cards (20 to 40) (PCMs 3 to 5), post-it notes

Spread the cards out face down. The children take a card each. They say what number should be added to that card to make the next multiple of ten. E.g. they take card 34. The answer is 6 (34 + **6** = 40). They write 6 on a post-it note and stick it on the 34 card. They each take another card and repeat the process until all the cards have been used.

N11 Money

ACTIVITY 1
Whole class, in pairs

- *Recognising coins and their value*
- *Matching numbers with coins*

Coins (two 1p, 2p, 5p, 10p, 20p) (one set per pair), number cards (1 to 30) (PCMs 2 to 4)

Shuffle the cards and place them in a pile face down. Take a card. Write the matching amount of money on the board, e.g. '16p'. Each pair has to show you that amount of money in the fewest coins possible. Every so often, ask for only one coin to match the amount. Each pair can choose to show you one coin of their choice.

ACTIVITY 2
3-4 children

- *Recognising coins and their value*
- *Matching a total with the fewest coins*

Coins (1p, 2p, 5p, 10p, 20p), a collection of toys, card for price labels (1p, 2p, 5p, 10p, 20p)

The children put a price label on each toy. They choose a toy, then each lay out the price of the toy using the fewest coins. The children check each other's totals. Have they used the fewest coins? Repeat for each toy.

ACTIVITY 3
3-4 children

- *Adding coins to find a total*
- *Matching a total using the fewest coins*

Coins (1p, 2p, 5p, 10p, 20p, 50p), felt-tipped pens

The children draw around one of their hands. They choose a coin (1p, 2p or 5p) and draw around that coin as many times as possible on the outline of their hand. They total up the coins, calculate how much their hand is 'worth' and write the total next to their hand. They work out how they could pay for their hand, using the fewest coins possible (up to 50p coins). E.g. a child chooses a 5p coin and fits 12 on his hand, so his hand is worth 60p. That amount could be given as one 50p coin and one 10p coin. Repeat, choosing a different coin to draw around.

ACTIVITY 4
3 children

- *Matching a total using the fewest coins*

Number cards (1 to 10) (PCM 2), coins (1p, 2p, 5p)

Spread out the cards face up. The children take turns to reveal a card, and match the card number using the fewest coins. E.g. 3 is matched by a 1p and a 2p coin, not three 1p coins. They take another card and repeat the process. At the end, every card should have a matching amount in coins. Together the children check they have used the fewest coins possible.

ACTIVITY 5
3 children

- *Adding different coins to make 20p*

Coins (1p, 2p, 5p, 10p, 20p)

Spread the coins out. The children write down as many ways as they can find to give someone 20p. Can they find them all? Encourage them to be systematic.

Multiplication

ACTIVITY 1
Whole class, in pairs

- *Recognising a given number of twos*
**Number cards (1 to 20)
(PCMs 2, 3)**
One pair agrees upon a
number, silently
counts in twos, using
their fingers, and
holds them up to
show how many twos
they have counted,
e.g. five. The other
pairs must select the
matching multiple
card, i.e. 10. Continue,
with different pairs.

ACTIVITY 2
3-4 children

- *Recognising and saying the multiples of two, in order*
Number cards (1 to 20) (PCMs 2, 3)
The children shuffle the cards and lay out the multiples of two, in order, up to
20, i.e. 2, 4, 6, etc. Ask them to say the multiples together *Two, four, six ...* They
reshuffle the cards and lay them out again. Extend the activity by laying out
the multiples of two in order. The children take turns to turn one card face
down while the others turn away, they turn back and have to guess which
number it is.

ACTIVITY 3
3-4 children

- *Recognising a given number of twos*
Number cards (1 to 10) (PCM 2), ten towers of two interlocking cubes
Shuffle the cards and place them face down. The children take turns to reveal a
card, match it with the same number of towers, and say how many cubes there
are. E.g. for card 7, they find seven towers and say *Seven twos are fourteen*.

ACTIVITY 4
3-4 children

- *Recognising a given number of twos*
- *Counting sets of 2p coins*
Number grid 1 (PCM 13), counters, 2p coins
The children cover each number on the grid with a counter. They take turns to
remove a counter, and multiply that number by two, e.g. for number 4, they
say *Four twos are eight*. If they are correct, they keep the counter, and take a
matching amount of coins, i.e. four 2p coins. Otherwise, they replace the
counter. The children continue until all the counters have been removed. The
winner is the player who collects the most money.

N13 **Multiplication**

ACTIVITY 1
Whole class, in pairs

• *Recognising a given number of tens*
Tens number cards (10 to 100) (PCM 9)
One pair agrees on a number (1 to 10), silently counts in tens, using that amount of fingers, and holds them up to show how many tens they have counted, e.g. seven. The other pairs have to select the matching multiple card, i.e. 70.
Continue, with different pairs.

ACTIVITY 2
3-4 children

• *Recognising and saying the multiples of ten, in order*
Tens cards (10 to 100) (PCM 9)
The children shuffle the cards and lay them out in order, up to 100, i.e. 10, 20, 30, etc. Ask them to say the multiples together *Ten, twenty, thirty ...* The children reshuffle the cards and lay them out again. Extend the activity by laying out the cards in order. The children take turns to turn one face down, whilst the others turn away. They turn back and then have to guess which number it is.

ACTIVITY 3
3-4 children

• *Recognising a given number of tens*
Number cards (1 to 10) (PCM 2), ten towers of ten interlocking cubes
Shuffle the cards and place them face down. The children take turns to reveal a card, match it with towers, and say how many cubes there are. E.g. for card 3, they find three towers, and say *Three tens are thirty*.

ACTIVITY 4
3-4 children

• *Recognising a given number of tens*
• *Counting sets of 10p coins*
Number grid 1 (PCM 13), counters, 10p coins
The children cover each number on the grid with a counter. They take turns to remove a counter, and multiply that number by ten, e.g. for number 6, they say *Six tens are sixty*. If they are correct, they keep the counter, and take a matching amount of coins, i.e. 60p. Otherwise, they replace the counter. The children continue until all the counters have been removed. The winner is the player who collects the most money.

ACTIVITY 1
Whole class, in pairs

- *Dividing a square into quarters in different ways, by folding*
Square sheets of paper, scissors
The pairs each have a sheet of paper. They fold it to make two halves, then fold it again to make four quarters. They cut along the fold lines and place the four parts on top of one another to check that they are the same. Can they make quarters in other ways? Ask them to investigate the possibilities.

ACTIVITY 2
3-4 children

- *Dividing a square into quarters in different ways, by cutting*
- *Recognising whether or not a shape has been divided into quarters*
Square sheets of paper, scissors, crayons
The children fold the paper to make quarters and colour each quarter a different colour. They cut along the folds and piece the quarters together like a jigsaw. How many different patterns can they make? They must check that the quarters are the same size.

ACTIVITY 3
3-4 children

- *Dividing different shapes into quarters, by folding*
A set of 2-d shapes (squares, rectangles, circles, triangles), paper, scissors
The children draw around a shape on paper and cut it out. They fold the paper to make halves, and again to make quarters. They write 'quarter' in each quarter section. The children must sort the shapes into those which can be folded into four quarters and those which cannot. Display the shapes, and write the shape names alongside.

ACTIVITY 4
3-4 children

- *Investigating different ways of dividing a 4 x 4 grid into four quarters*
4 x 4 square grids (PCM 18), crayons
Ask the children to explore different ways of dividing the grid into four quarters. They colour each quarter, using a different colour. How many different ways can they find to split the grid into quarters? Let them investigate the possibilities.

ACTIVITY 1
Whole class, in pairs

- *Counting in tens starting from any number up to 10*
Number cards (1 to 100) (PCMs 2 to 8), two dice (cover the sixes), 10p coins
Give each pair three cards at random. Throw one or two dice to obtain a number between one and ten. Start on that number and count, with the children, in tens. If you say a number held by a pair, they receive a 10p coin. Throw the dice again and repeat. Continue until one pair has collected £1.

ACTIVITY 2
4 children

- *Counting in tens starting from any number up to 10*
Number cards (1 to 100) (PCMs 2 to 8)
Lay out all the cards face up on the table. Each child chooses a different starting number, less than 10, e.g. 4. They lay out a line of cards, starting with that number, and counting up in tens, i.e. 4, 14, 24 ... The children check each other's lines. Are any numbers missing?

ACTIVITY 3
3-4 children

- *Recognising the place-value of digits in 2-digit numbers*
- *Matching 2-digit numbers to coins*
Place-value cards (tens, units) (PCMs 10 to 12), coins (1p, 10p)
The children shuffle the cards and place them in two piles (tens and units) face down. They each take a card from each pile, create a 2-digit number and compare their numbers. Whose is the largest? Whose is the smallest? They collect 10p and 1p coins to match their number and place them on the number. Repeat, taking a new card from each pile.

ACTIVITY 4
3 children

- *Counting in tens from a 3-digit number*
Number cards (1 to 9) (PCM 2)
The children spread out the cards face up. They take turns to reveal a card. They put the three cards together to make a 3-digit number. They count in tens from that number, writing each new number until they reach the next hundred. E.g. they reveal cards 4, 7 and 3, creating 473. They write 473, 483, 493, **5**03. They use the same three cards to make a new 3-digit number, e.g. 347, and repeat the process, e.g. 347, 357, 367, 377, 387, 397, **4**07. How many numbers can they make using just three cards?

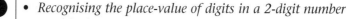

ACTIVITY 1
Whole class, in groups of 3

- *Recognising the place-value of digits in a 2-digit number*
- *Partitioning a number into tens and units*

Number cards (1 to 100) (PCMs 2 to 8), coins (1p, 10p)

Take a card at random and write the number on the board. The groups match it with 10p and 1p coins. Discuss each number and check that the amounts of money are correct. Repeat several times.

ACTIVITY 2
3 children

- *Recognising the place-value of digits in a 2-digit number*
- *Partitioning a number into tens and units*

Place-value cards (tens and units) (PCMs 10 to 12), number cards (1 to 99) (PCMs 2 to 8)

One child picks a card (1 to 99) e.g. 39. The others find the matching tens and units cards, i.e. 30 and 9. The children continue, sharing the roles.

ACTIVITY 3
4 children

- *Partitioning a number into tens and units*
- *Recognising the largest tens/units digit*

Place-value cards (tens and units) (PCMs 10 to 12), counters

The cards are shuffled and placed face down in two piles. Each child takes one tens card and one units card and creates a 2-digit number. They take turns to say each number, and how many tens and units are in the number. The child with the largest tens digit takes a counter and the child with the largest units digit takes a counter. The children replace the cards and repeat, several times. Who collects the most counters?

ACTIVITY 4
3 children

- *Recognising the largest of a set of 2-digit numbers*
- *Partitioning a number into tens and units*

Two sets of number cards (1 to 9) (PCM 2), coins (1p, 10p), counters

Shuffle each set of cards and place them face down in two piles. One child takes a card from each pile, e.g. 6 and 4. He makes a 2-digit number, e.g. 64. The other two children do the same. They look at the numbers they have created and the child with the largest number takes a counter. They check, by matching each number using 10p and 1p coins. The children replace the cards and play again.

ACTIVITY 5
3-4 children

- *Recognising the value of digits in a 2-digit number*

A dice, Base Ten equipment (tens and units)

The children take turns to throw the dice. They take a matching number of units and place them in a line. When they have ten units they exchange them for a ten. The winner is the first child to collect three tens.

ACTIVITY 1
Whole class, in pairs

• *Adding near doubles (up to 10)*
Two sets of number cards (1 to 10) (PCM 2), a ten-sided dice, interlocking cubes
Give each pair a number card. Roll the dice and read out the number. If that number is adjacent to any pair's card number, they add the two numbers together and tell you the total. E.g. you throw a 6, so any pair with a 5 or a 7 may add 5 + 6 or 6 + 7 and say the answer. If they are correct, they take a cube. Play until one pair has three cubes.

ACTIVITY 2
3 children

• *Doubling numbers (up to 5)*
Number cards (1 to 5) (PCM 2), interlocking cubes, post-it notes
The children lay out the cards in order. They build a tower of cubes to match each card. They choose a number and double it by doubling the number of cubes in the tower. They count the new total of cubes and write it on a post-it note. They stick the note on the number card and repeat.

ACTIVITY 3
2-3 children

• *Doubling amounts of coins (up to 10p)*
Number cards (1 to 10) (PCM 2), coins (1p, 5p, 10p), post-it notes
The children shuffle the cards and place them in a pile face down. They take a card from the pile, read the number and match it with the correct number of coins. They double that amount by taking another set of the same coins. If they have two 5p coins or ten 1p coins they can exchange them for a 10p coin. They write the double on a post-it note and stick it on the card.

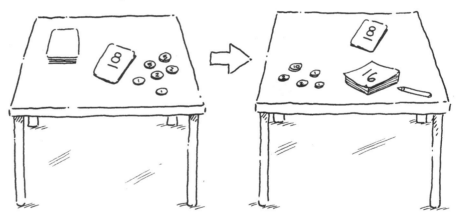

ACTIVITY 4
3 children

• *Doubling amounts of coins (up to 20p)*
Number cards (10 to 20) (PCMs 2, 3), coins (1p, 5p, 10p), post-it notes
The children spread out the cards face up. They take turns to pick a card, match the amount shown on the card in coins and then double it. Can they work out what the double is? They may have to exchange two 5p coins for a 10p, etc. They write the double on a post-it note and stick it on the card.

N18 Addition

ACTIVITY 1
Whole class, in pairs

• *Adding by counting on*
Sets of number cards (6 to 10) (PCM 2), a dice, interlocking cubes
Give each pair a card. Throw a dice and read out the number. Each pair must say the number that adds to the dice number to make their card number. E.g. they have card number 6 and the dice number is 2. They must say *Four* (4 added to 2 makes 6). If they are correct, they receive a cube. Repeat several times.

ACTIVITY 2
3 children

• *Finding addition and subtraction pairs for numbers up to 10*
Two sets of number cards (0 to 10) (PCM 2), post-it notes
Ask the children to lay out the cards face up. They choose a number between 5 and 10 and find all the different pairs of cards which total that number. E.g. they choose 7, and they find 3 and 4, 2 and 5, 1 and 6 and 0 and 7. They write all the pairs on a post-it note and stick it on the table. Ask them to start again with a different number and repeat the process. Repeat, choosing a number between 1 and 4, finding all the pairs with that difference.

ACTIVITY 3
2-3 children

• *Finding addition pairs for numbers up to 10*
Number cards (5 to 10) (PCM 2), interlocking cubes in two colours
Shuffle the cards and place them in a pile face down. The children take a card from the pile. They read the number and build a tower of cubes to match the number using one colour. Each child then builds other towers of the same height, using two colours (in blocks, i.e. not alternate). No two towers should be the same in terms of the number of cubes in each colour. They look at all their towers and write down the matching additions, e.g. '5 + 1 = 6', '4 + 2 = 6', '3 + 3 = 6'. Repeat the process, choosing a new card.

ACTIVITY 4
3 children

• *Finding addition pairs for numbers up to 10*
Several sets of number cards (1 to 9) (PCM 2)
The children spread out the cards face up. They take a card with 8, 9 or 10 on. Explain that you want them to build a number wall for that card. They must select two cards which, when added together, total the number on the first card. They place these cards below it. Next, they must select a pair of cards for each card in the second row and again place them below. E.g.

They continue until they have built five different walls for 9. Repeat, building walls for the numbers 8 and 10.

 Subtraction

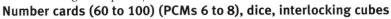

ACTIVITY 1
Whole class, in pairs

- *Subtracting multiples of 10*
Number cards (60 to 100) (PCMs 6 to 8), dice, interlocking cubes
Write '50' on the board. Give each pair a card. Throw a dice and read out the number. Each pair subtracts that number of **tens** from their card number, e.g. they have the 68 card and the dice shows two. They should subtract 20 (68 – 20 = 48). The pair whose answer is nearest to 50 receives a cube. Repeat several times.

ACTIVITY 2
3-4 children

- *Subtracting 13 from a 2-digit number (up to 50)*
One set of number cards (25 to 30, 35 to 40, 45 to 50) (PCMs 4, 5), coins (1p, 10p), one set of number cards (1 to 100) (PCMs 2 to 8)
The children select a card from the first pile, e.g. 36. They match it with coins, i.e. three 10p coins and six 1p coins. They subtract 13 from the number and find the card in the second pile that matches the answer, i.e. 23, placing it beside the first card. The children repeat the activity six more times so that there are seven pairs of cards, where the difference is 13.

ACTIVITY 3
2-3 children

- *Subtracting multiples of 10*
Number cards (20 to 50) (PCMs 3 to 5), coins (1p, 10p)
The children shuffle the cards and place them in a pile face down. They take a card from the pile. They read the number and match it with 10p and 1p coins. One child subtracts either 10, 20 or 30, taking away the 10p coin(s) without showing the others how much he has taken. The others look at the remaining coins and have to say what the total was and how much was subtracted. All the children write down the matching subtraction. E.g. the card says 36, the child takes away 20p and there is 16p left. The children write '36 – 20 = 16'. They take another card from the pile and play again.

ACTIVITY 4
Pairs

- *Subtracting 11, 12, 13 or 14 from a 2-digit number*
Card to write pairs of numbers (75, 40), (89, 50) (86, 51), (99, 60), (85, 52), (79, 43), (69, 30), (109, 72), (82, 49)
The children choose one of the pairs of numbers, e.g. 89 and 50. They must write three subtractions to get from the higher number to the lower. They can subtract 11, 12, 13 or 14 each time, but they must only take three steps. They can use the numbers more than once.

ACTIVITY 5
3-4 children

- *Subtracting 1-digit numbers from numbers up to 36*
Infant game 17: 'On the hop', dice, counters, two sets of number cards (0 to 10) (PCM 2)
(See instructions on the card.)

N20 Numbers to 100

ACTIVITY 1
Whole class, in pairs

- *Counting on in steps of two, three, four, five or ten (up to 50)*
Number cards (1 to 50) (PCMs 2 to 5), interlocking cubes
Give each pair two number cards. Decide, with the children, to count in twos, threes, fours, fives or tens. Start counting in unison. If you say a number which a pair has on one of their cards, they must stand up. When you pass 50, stop counting. All the children standing up receive a cube. Repeat, counting in different steps.

ACTIVITY 2
3 children

- *Counting on in steps of three, four or five*
Number cards (1 to 50) (PCMs 2 to 5), card (to make additional number cards)
One child must choose to count in steps of three, another in steps of four and another in steps of five. Each child must lay out the cards which match the numbers in their counting steps. E.g. if they are counting in fours, they lay out 4, 8, 12, 16 ... in order up to 48. There will be cards which more than one child wants. In such cases, the children will have to make extra cards using the blank card. How many extra cards do they have to make? Which cards are they?

ACTIVITY 3
2-3 children

- *Counting in fives (up to 50)*
Number cards (1 to 50) (PCMs 2 to 5), 5p coins
The children spread out the cards face up. They work together to choose the card numbers which occur when counting in fives. They arrange them in a line, e.g. 5, 10, 15, 20 ... They put one 5p coin on the first card, two on the second, and so on. How much money is there, in total, on each card? (It should match the card number.)

ACTIVITY 4
Pairs

- *Counting in threes, fours or fives*
Number cards (1 to 100) (PCMs 2 to 8), number grid (1 to 100) (PCM 19)
The children have to select the cards, up to 100, which are used when counting in threes, fours and fives. Which numbers are common to all three counts? Colour a number grid to help.

ACTIVITY 1
Whole class, in pairs

• *Writing calculations for real life 'mathematical' situations*
Number cards (1 to 9) (PCM 2), card for sign labels (+, –, =)
Make up a simple number story. E.g. *Jane has five sweets and Mohammed has seven. How many more has Mohammed?* The children have to tell the story using their cards and lay out the calculation that will produce the answer. (There may well be more than one way of finding the answer.) Discuss the different ways children have tackled the problem and write one or two ways on the board, e.g. '5 + ☐ = 7' and '7 – 5 = ?'. Start again with a different story, e.g. *There were six ducks on a pond and two more flew down and one dived under to eat some weed. How many ducks on the pond?*

ACTIVITY 2
2 pairs

• *Calculating the difference between two numbers (up to 20)*
Several number tracks (numbered 1 to 20) (PCM 1 photocopied twice)
Give each pair a number track. Ask the children to choose two numbers on their track, one more than 10 and one less than 10 and write them down, e.g. 15 and 8. They cross out the numbers on the track which are more than their largest number (i.e. 16, 17, 18, 19, 20) and colour the numbers up to and including their smallest number (i.e. 1, 2, 3, 4, 5, 6, 7, 8). They work out the difference between their two numbers and write it below their two original numbers (i.e. 7). The pairs now swap their two numbers, and check each other's answers, using a different track. Do they agree what the difference is? Repeat, starting with two new tracks and two different numbers.

ACTIVITY 3
2-3 children

• *Calculating the difference between two numbers (up to 20)*
Number track (numbered 1 to 20) (PCM 1), number cards (10 to 19)
(PCMs 2, 3), post-it notes, interlocking cubes
Shuffle the cards and place them in a pile face down. The children turn over a card. They work together to calculate what number needs to be added to the card number, to make 20. They do this by placing a cube on every number on the track up to the card number. E.g. if the card number is 15, they place cubes on the track from 1 to 15. How many spaces on the track do NOT have cubes? This is how many more are needed to make 20. They write that number on a post-it note and stick it on the card. They take another card and repeat.

ACTIVITY 4
3 children

• *Pairing numbers with a difference of nine*
Number cards (1 to 30) (PCMs 2 to 4)
The children have to work out how many pairs of cards they can make which have a difference of 9, e.g. 21 and 30. How many pairs are there? Can the children find out how many pairs of numbers have a difference of 11?

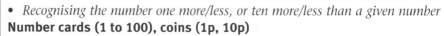

ACTIVITY 1
Whole class in groups of 3

- *Recognising the number one more/less, or ten more/less than a given number*
Number cards (1 to 100), coins (1p, 10p)
Take a card at random and write the number on the board. Decide whether to say; one less, one more, ten less or ten more. The groups match the answers with 10p and 1p coins. Discuss the answer and check the amounts of money are correct. Repeat several times.

ACTIVITY 2
4 children

- *Recognising the number one more/less, or ten more/less than a given number*
Number cards (10 to 30) (PCMs 2 to 4), number grid (1 to 100) (PCM 19), counters
The children take turns to reveal a card, and say the number which is one more. The children should check each other's answers, using the number grid if necessary. If they are correct, they keep the card. The children continue through the cards. Who collects the most cards? Repeat the activity by asking for the numbers which are one less, ten more or ten less.

ACTIVITY 3
3 children

- *Recognising the number ten more/less than a given number*
- *Combining different amounts of money using 10p and 1p coins*
Place-value cards (tens and units) (PCMs 10 to 12), coins (1p, 10p)
Shuffle the place-value cards and spread them out, face down. The children take turns to reveal a tens and a units card, say the 2-digit number, then say the number ten more. If they are correct, they collect a matching amount of money. E.g. they turn over a 30 and a 3, say, *Forty-three* and collect 43p. Repeat three times each. Who collects the most money? Who has the least? Repeat for another three rounds.

ACTIVITY 4
3 children

- *Recognising 1p more/less, 10p more/less than an amount of money*
Number cards (10 to 50) (PCMs 2 to 5), coins (1p, 10p), card for labels ('1p more', '1p less', '10p more', '10p less')
Shuffle the number cards and put them in a pile face down. Do the same with the card labels. Ask each child to take one card from each pile, and collect a matching amount of money. E.g. for cards 31, and 10 less, they collect 21p. Ask them to check each other's money. Who has collected the most? Who has the least? Repeat several times.

ACTIVITY 5
2-3 children

- *Recognising the number ten more/less than a given number*
- *Beginning to recognise the number which is twenty more/less than a given number*
Number grid (1 to 100) (PCM 19), counters, interlocking cubes
Ask the children to place 20 counters on the grid covering up the numbers. One child points at a square and the player to his left has to say the hidden number, then a number which is ten more. If he is correct, he collects a cube, and removes the counter. The children take turns until all the counters have been removed. Who has the most cubes? Extend the activity by asking the children to say numbers which are ten less (or 20 more and 20 less).

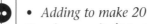 Addition

ACTIVITY 1
Whole class, in pairs

- *Adding to make 20*
Number cards (1 to 9) (PCM 2), large number line (1 to 20)
The children draw three circles and write a 'teen' number in each. Shuffle the cards and place them in a pile face down. Turn over a card. The children say which number adds to the card number to make 20. If a pair have that number in a circle they may cross it out. Turn over another card and repeat. The first pair to cross out all three circles can shout *Bingo!* Use the number line to help.

ACTIVITY 2
3 children

- *Adding a 1-digit number to a 'teen' number*
- *Matching coins to given amounts using the fewest coins*
Two sets of number cards (10 to 20) (PCMs 2, 3), card for labels ('+', '='), a dice, coins (1p, 2p, 5p, 10p, 20p), number line (1 to 20)
Shuffle the cards and place them in a pile face down. One child turns over a card. He lays it on the table and places the '+' card next to it. The second child throws the dice. She writes the matching number on a piece of paper and places it next to the '+' card. The third child places the '=' card next to the written number and calculates the answer. The other two check he is correct. They match the answer to coins, using the fewest coins possible. Leaving the cards and money to one side, they start again, with a different child taking a card. Repeat several times. Use the number line to help.

ACTIVITY 3
2 pairs

- *Adding two numbers to total up to 20*
- *Matching 'teen' numbers to a ten and units*
Two sets of number cards (5 to 15) (PCMs 2, 3), card for labels (two sets of '+', '='), post-it notes, interlocking cubes, large number line (1 to 20)
Shuffle the number cards and place them in a pile face down. Each pair turns over two cards. They work together to set out an addition using the cubes. They should put the larger number first and build towers of ten where possible. For instance, 14 + 3 would be a tower of ten and four loose cubes, plus three loose cubes. They place the sign card between the cubes to create an addition. Finally, they write the answer on a post-it note and stick it in position. Each pair checks the other pair's calculation. They take two new cards each and repeat. Use the number line to help.

ACTIVITY 4
3 children

- *Pairing numbers to total 40 (and 50)*
Number cards (1 to 50) (PCMs 2 to 5)
The children calculate how many pairs of cards they can make with a total of 40, e.g. 2 and 38. What is the total number of pairs? How many pairs of cards have a total of 50?

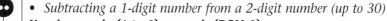

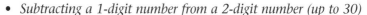

N24 **Subtraction**

ACTIVITY 1
Whole class, in pairs

- *Subtracting a 1-digit number from a 2-digit number (up to 30)*

Number cards (1 to 9) per pair (PCM 2)

Ask each pair to draw three circles and write a 'teen' number in each. On the board, write a number between 20 and 28 and a minus sign, e.g. '23 –'. Shuffle the cards and place them in a pile face down. Ask the children to turn over a card. Each pair takes their card number away from the number on the board. Is the answer in one of their circles? If so, that pair may cross through their circle. Repeat until one pair has crossed out all three circles and shouts *Bingo!*

ACTIVITY 2
3 children

- *Subtracting a 1-digit number from a 2-digit number (up to 30)*
- *Matching coins to given amounts using the fewest coins*

Number cards (11 to 30) (PCMs 3, 4), card for labels ('–', '='), a dice, coins (1p, 2p, 5p, 10p, 20p)

Shuffle the cards and place them in a pile face down. One child turns over a card. He lays it on the table and places the '–' card next to it. The second child rolls the dice. He writes the matching number on a piece of paper and places it next to the '–' card. The third child then places the '=' card next to the written number and calculates the answer. The other two check it is correct. They match the answer to the fewest coins possible. Leaving the cards and money to one side, they start again with a different child taking a card. Repeat several times.

ACTIVITY 3
3 children

- *Subtracting a 1-digit number from a 2-digit number (up to 99)*
- *Recognising nearest multiples of 10*

Place-value cards (tens, units) (PCMs 10 to 12), number cards (0 to 9) (PCM 2)

Shuffle the tens cards and then the units cards and place them in two piles face down. Spread the number cards out face up. One child turns over a tens card and a units card and creates a 2-digit number. The second child has to choose the number card that when taken away from the 2-digit number leaves the nearest multiple of ten. The third child writes the calculation, e.g. '35 – 5 = 30'. They repeat, swapping roles. What do they notice?

ACTIVITY 4
3 children

- *Recognising the place-value of digits (up to 29)*
- *Subtracting 1-digit numbers from 2-digit numbers to leave a multiple of 10*
- *Matching coins to a given amount using 10p and 1p coins*

Place-value cards (units, 10, 20) (PCMs 10 to 12), coins (1p, 10p), post-it notes

Spread the cards out face up on the table. Taking two cards, one child makes a teen number, e.g. using 10 and 6 to make 16. The next child takes this amount in coins, i.e. one 10p and six 1ps. The third child has to take away the 1p coins to leave only 10p. How many does she have to take away? She writes that number on a post-it note and sticks it on the table beside the number. They repeat, taking different roles.

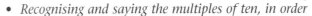N25 **Multiplication**

ACTIVITY 1
Whole class, in groups of 3-4

- *Recognising and saying the multiples of ten, in order*
- *Recognising and saying the multiples of five, in order*

Tens cards (10 to 100) (PCM 9) (one set per group), fives cards (5 to 50) (PCMs 2 to 5) (one set per group)

Shuffle the tens cards and ask the groups to lay them out, in order, up to 100, i.e. 10, 20, 30 …The whole class says the multiples *Ten, twenty, thirty* … Ask them to reshuffle the cards and lay them out again. Repeat using the fives cards.

ACTIVITY 2
3 children

- *Recognising a given number of twos, fives and tens*

Number cards (1 to 100) (PCMs 2 to 8), tens number cards (10, 20 … 100) (PCM 9), extra number cards (10, 20) (PCM 9), a ten-sided dice, counters

The children choose multiples of 2, 5 or 10. Using the number cards, they each make a track to match their first ten multiples, e.g. 2, 4, 6 … 20 or 5, 10, 15 … 50. They check each other's tracks. They take turns to throw the dice and cover that number of fives, twos or tens with a counter. Who is the first to cover all their numbers?

ACTIVITY 3
3 children

- *Recognising a given number of fives and tens*

Infant game 18: 'Snake tables', number cards (1 to 10) (PCM 2), counters

(See instructions on the card.)

ACTIVITY 4
3 children

- *Recognising multiplication facts involving 2, ×5 and ×10 tables*
- *Using a calculator to find multiplication facts to ×2, ×5 and ×10 tables*

Number cards (1 to 50) (PCMs 2 to 5), a calculator

One child enters, on the calculator, a multiplication from the ×2, ×5 or ×10 tables, e.g. 4 × 5. The others calculate the answer, and select the matching number card. They place it face down on the table without showing the first child, who then completes the calculation on the calculator, i.e. = 20. They turn over the card. Does it match the answer on the calculator? The children repeat several times, sharing the roles.

ACTIVITY 5
3 children

- *Recognising a given number of twos, fives and tens*

Number cards (1 to 10) (PCM 2)

Shuffle the cards and place them face down in a pile. The children choose to concentrate on either the ×2, ×5 or ×10 table. One of them turns over the top card, e.g. 7. The 'twos' child says *Seven twos are fourteen*. The 'fives' child says *Seven fives are thirty-five*. The 'tens' child says *Seven tens are seventy*. Continue until all the cards have been turned over. The children can repeat the activity, choosing a different number to multiply.

ACTIVITY 1
Whole class, in pairs

- *Dividing a quantity by sharing equally*
Interlocking cubes, a dice
Roll the dice and write the number on the board, e.g. '3'. Each pair takes a handful of cubes and shares them between three. Which pairs can share their cubes equally? Which can't? Write some of the numbers on the board. Repeat.

ACTIVITY 2
2-3 children

- *Dividing a quantity by sharing equally*
36 interlocking cubes
The children share the cubes into four equal groups. They check that each group is the same by building a tower. They count the cubes in each tower and write the number.
Repeat, sharing the cubes between nine, six, three and two groups.

ACTIVITY 3
2-3 children

- *Dividing a quantity by sharing equally*
24 counters
The children share the counters into six equal piles. They count the counters in each pile and write the number. Ask them to repeat the activity, sharing the counters between eight, four, three and two piles.

ACTIVITY 4
3 children

- *Dividing a quantity by sharing equally between different amounts*
Number grid 3 (PCM 15), ten red and ten blue counters, interlocking cubes
The children work together, placing a red counter on any number on the grid that shares equally into three. They count out each matching number of cubes and try to share them equally between themselves to check. Repeat, placing a blue counter on each number that shares equally into four, then checking with cubes. Do any numbers have a blue and a red counter?

ACTIVITY 5
2-3 children

- *Investigating different ways of sharing a given quantity between different amounts*
Coins (30 × 1p)
Ask the children to investigate how many ways they can equally share the 30 coins i.e. groups of 1, 2, 3, 5, 6, 10, 15, 30.

N27 **Fractions**

ACTIVITY 1
Whole class, in pairs

- *Recognising halves*
- *Exploring different ways to solve a problem*

Different symmetrical paper shapes (use PCM 21 enlarged to A3), scissors
The pairs cut out each shape, fold the shapes to make two halves and then cut along the fold. They place one half over the other to check they are the same. Are there any shapes which don't fold into half? Can any shapes be folded a different way?

ACTIVITY 2
3-4 children

- *Recognising halves and quarters of shapes*
- *Understanding that some shapes cannot be folded into two halves*
- *Naming common 2-d shapes*

2-d shapes (squares, rectangles, circles, triangles) (or use PCM 21), scissors
The children draw round a shape on paper, cut it out, then fold it in half. They write 'half' and '½' on each half of the shape. Ask them to sort the shapes into those which can be folded into two halves and those which cannot. Display the shapes, and write the names alongside. Extend the activity by asking them to fold the shapes to make quarters.

ACTIVITY 3
3-4 children

- *Dividing a square grid into two halves, and into four quarters*
- *Exploring and creating different solutions to a problem*

4 x 4 square grids (PCM 18), crayons (two colours)
Ask the children to colour half of each grid in different ways. How many ways can they find to colour the grids? Let them investigate the possibilities. Extend the activity by asking them to colour the four quarters of each grid in different ways (using four colours).

ACTIVITY 4
Pair

- *Recognising fraction notation ($\frac{1}{2}$, $\frac{1}{4}$, $\frac{1}{3}$)*

Concept keyboard with a word processor (create overlay and file to match)
The children take turns to match a fraction to a fraction name, e.g. 'a half' matches '½', and then to the appropriate picture. They write down their answers and compare.

a half	$\frac{1}{3}$	
a third	$\frac{1}{4}$	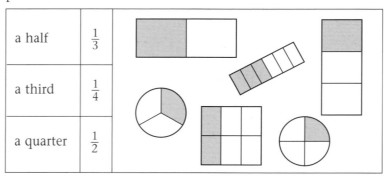
a quarter	$\frac{1}{2}$	

ACTIVITY 5
Pairs

- *Dividing a square grid into halves, quarters and thirds*

2 cm squared paper
Draw several grids 2 × 6 and investigate colouring halves, quarters and thirds. Label each section. Repeat using 3 × 4 grids.

N28 Numbers to 100

ACTIVITY 1
Whole class

- *Counting/reciting numbers (up to 100)*

Ask the whole class to count silently, starting at one. After a short while, stop them and ask one child to write down on a piece of paper the number he has reached. Ask him to show you the number. Ask the rest of the class what numbers they counted to. Write down their numbers under the appropriate range headings on the board. Then reveal the number that was written down on the paper. Whose number was closest? Repeat the activity several times. Repeat, slowly counting in fives or tens.

ACTIVITY 2
4 children

- *Counting (up to 55)*
- *Reasoning about numbers and organising ideas*
- *Recognising addition pairs to 10*

Playing cards (Aces to tens)
Each child chooses a suit. The children work together to estimate and then to count the number of symbols on the cards, i.e. the total number of spades on all the spades cards in the suit (55). Point out to them that they should only count the symbols in the centre of the card, not the smaller ones under the corner numbers. What do they notice?
Ask them to use all the cards to match pairs which make ten and count these (22 including ten and no card). Note how they approach the problem. They have to agree an answer and show how they reached that total.

ACTIVITY 3
3 children

- *Recognising tens and units in 2-digit numbers*

Place-value cards (tens, units) (PCMs 10 to 12), interlocking cubes, (red and blue) counters
Spread the place-value cards out face up on the table. One child turns over a tens and a units card and creates a 2-digit number. The other children count out that number of cubes or counters. They should count in tens and then add the units. They use the tens card to help them remember how many tens there are. They place a red counter on the number if it is odd, a blue counter if it is even and place the number to one side.
Repeat, swapping roles.

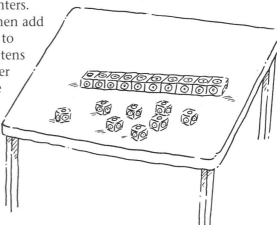

ACTIVITY 4
3 children

- *Recognising the value of the tens digit in a 2-digit number*

Place-value cards (tens, units) (PCMs 10 to 12), picture books, cubes
The children work out how many words there are in the whole book, using a tallying system involving the place-value cards. Every time they have counted ten words, they indicate it by changing the tens card. Ask them to check their total, counting from the back to the front. Repeat with a different book, but this time tallying in fives on paper. Every time they have counted five words, they take a cube.

Ordering

ACTIVITY 1
Whole class, in pairs

- *Ordering a set of 1- and 2-digit numbers*
Number cards (1 to 30)
Each pair draws a grid of four horizontal squares ⬜⬜⬜⬜. Pick a number card at random and read it aloud. Each pair writes the number on their grid. Pick three more cards. The pairs should try to ensure their four numbers are in order, smallest to largest. Once they have written a number they cannot move it. Discuss the order of the four numbers. Repeat.

ACTIVITY 2
4-5 children

- *Ordering a set of 1- and 2-digit numbers*
Number cards (1 to 50) (PCMs 2 to 5), number grid (1 to 100) (PCM 19), counters
The children shuffle the cards and place them face down. They select a card each, and place them in order from smallest to largest. Use the number grid to check the order, if necessary. Ask them to decide whose number is the smallest and whose is the largest. The children whose numbers fall in between collect a counter each. Continue, playing several rounds, and see who collects the most counters.

ACTIVITY 3
4-5 children

- *Ordering a set of 2-digit numbers*
- *Locating position of numbers on a number track*
Place-value cards (tens, units) (PCMs 10 to 12), blank number track (PCM 1), counters
The children start by marking their number track in tens along the lines: 0, 10, 20 ... 100. They spread out the place-value cards, face down, then each select one tens and one units card to create a 2-digit number. The children take turns to be the 'marker' who locates the number position on their number track. They use the number track to order the numbers from smallest to largest. The holders of the smallest and largest numbers collect a counter. Continue, playing several rounds, and see who collects the most counters.

ACTIVITY 4
4-5 children

- *Ordering different amounts of money*
Coins (1p, 10p), a feely bag, number grid (1 to 100) (PCM 19), counters, interlocking cubes
The children place the coins in the bag and draw out a handful each. They count how much money they each have in total and place a counter on the matching number on the number grid. They check each other's counting. The children put the sums of money in order from smallest to largest, using the number grid to help. All the children, except those with the smallest and largest amounts of money, collect a cube. Repeat several times. Who collects the most cubes?

ACTIVITY 5
Pairs

- *Ordering a large set of 1- and 2-digit numbers*
- *Collecting, processing and presenting data*
Interlocking cubes, counters, other counting materials
Collect information about the children's house or flat numbers. They find ways of recording the information, then present the numbers in order from smallest to largest. How many have the same house or flat number?

ACTIVITY 1
Whole class, in pairs

• *Adding three numbers to make 20*
Several sets of number cards (1 to 9) (PCM 2), interlocking cubes
Write '20' on the board. Give each pair three cards and ask them to find the total. How close are they to 20? Does any pair have exactly 20? If so, they take a cube. Each pair swaps one of their cards for a new one. They calculate their new total. Does any pair now have a total of exactly 20? Repeat several times.

ACTIVITY 2
3 children

• *Adding three numbers (up to 40)*
Two sets of number cards (4 to 14) (PCMs 2, 3)
Each child chooses a card. They have to work together to add the numbers on their three cards. They should look for pairs which make ten when added together. If there are no such pairs, they start with the larger number and bridge the ten. They have to agree an answer between them and then each writes down the calculation, e.g. '12 + 6 + 3 = 21'. Repeat with a different card each.

ACTIVITY 3
3 children

• *Adding three numbers to total up to 20*
Number tracks (1 to 20) (PCM 1, photocopied twice), two sets of number cards (2 to 7) (PCM 2), counters (two colours)
Shuffle the cards and place them face down on the table. The children each reveal a card. Do any two cards total exactly ten? If so, they add them and make ten, then add on the third card number. If not, they decide which of the cards has the largest number. On the number track, they put a counter in the spaces up to and including that number. They take the next largest number and continue along the track putting a counter in a matching number of spaces. When they reach ten, they should change colour. Finally, they do the same with the smallest card number. What is their total? They return the cards, and start again, repeating the process.

ACTIVITY 4
3 children

• *Adding three numbers to total 20*
Number cards (1 to 20) (PCMs 2, 3)
The children have to work out how many sets of three numbers they can find which total 20. How many sets can they find which total 21?

Addition/subtraction

ACTIVITY 1
Whole class, in pairs

• *Adding pairs of numbers to make 20*
Number cards (1 to 9) per pair (PCM 2)
Ask each pair to draw three circles on their paper and to write a 'teen' number (11 to 19) in each. Shuffle the cards and place them in a pile face down. Pick a card. The pairs add the card number to the numbers in their circles. If they can total 20 with any circle, that circle is crossed out. Continue until one pair has crossed out all three circles.

ACTIVITY 2
3-4 children

• *Calculating change by subtracting from 10p and 20p*
Card for price labels (1p, 2p ... 19p), coins (1p, 2p, 5p, 10p, 20p)
Shuffle the price labels and place them face down in a pile. Each child takes two 10p and two 20p coins. They must leave the remaining coins on the table. The children take turns to reveal the top label from the pile, pay the amount with one coin, and take the correct change from the pile of money. They play three rounds, checking each other's change. How many coins does each child have left?

ACTIVITY 3
3 children

• *Adding coins to make 20*
Blank number track (numbered 1 to 20) (PCM 1, photocopied twice), coins (1p, 2p, 5p, 10p), cubes
One child takes an amount in coins, e.g. 5p. The second child finds the matching number on the track, i.e. 5. She puts a cube on this space. The third child counts out loud from that space to 20 to find out how much more money is needed to make 20p. They write the coin value and the number counted on the track to make 20p as an addition, i.e. '5p + 15p = 20p'. They repeat, swapping roles.

ACTIVITY 4
3 children

• *Making 20p using coins*
Coins (1p, 2p, 5p, 10p)
How many different ways can the children find of giving someone 20p using 1p, 2p, 5p and 10p coins? Ask the children to write down each way. Have they found every way? Can they show that they have?

ACTIVITY 5
3 children

• *Adding pairs of numbers to make 100*
Tens cards, two sets (PCM 9), coins (10p, £1)
Shuffle the cards and lay them face up on the table. The children take turns to pick a pair of cards to make 100. When all the cards are used, they match each card with 10p coins and add the coins for each pair of cards, to check. If correct, they swap the 10p coins for a £1 coin.

N32 Addition

ACTIVITY 1
Whole class, in pairs

- *Doubling numbers (up to 15)*
Number cards (1 to 15) (PCMs 2, 3), interlocking cubes
Each pair gives you a target number (an even number between 2 and 30). Write the numbers on the board with the children's initials against each one. Shuffle the cards and place them in a pile face down. Turn over a card and say the number. The children must double this number and write down the answer. If the number is their target number, they can take a cube. Repeat, with new target numbers.

ACTIVITY 2
3 children

- *Doubling numbers (up to 15)*
- *Matching coins to amounts (up to 30p)*
Number cards (1 to 15) (PCMs 2, 3), coins (1p, 2p, 5p, 10p), post-it notes
Shuffle the number cards and place them in a pile face down. One child turns over a card. The second child takes that amount in coins. The third child doubles the number by taking another, equal amount in coins. They find the total amount. The first child writes the answer on a post-it note and sticks it on the card. They leave the card and money to one side and repeat, with a different child taking a card.

ACTIVITY 3
3 children

- *Doubling numbers (up to 10)*
Number cards (1 to 10) (PCM 2), interlocking cubes
Shuffle the cards and place them in a pile face down. One child turns over a card and takes that number of cubes. The second child has to take an equal number of cubes. The third child writes down the doubling calculation, e.g. '5 + 5 = 10'. They repeat, swapping roles.

ACTIVITY 4
3 children

- *Trebling numbers (up to 12)*
- *Matching coins to amounts (up to 36p)*
Number cards (1 to 12) (PCMs 2, 3), coins (1p, 2p, 5p, 10p)
Spread the cards out face up on the table. One child takes a card, e.g. 7. The second child takes this amount in coins, e.g. one 5p and two 1ps. The third child takes two lots of the same number of coins and writes down the addition, i.e. '7 + 7 + 7 =', to calculate the answer. Repeat, swapping roles.

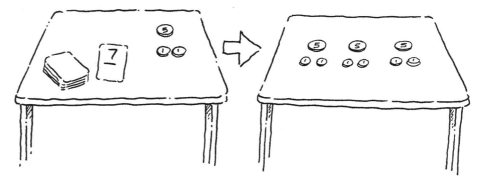

ACTIVITY 5
3 children

- *Doubling multiples of five to 50*
Fives cards (5, 10, 15... 50) (PCMs 2 to 5), tens cards (PCM 9), coins (5p)
Shuffle all the cards and spread them out on the table, face down. The children play pelmanism, taking turns to reveal two cards. If one card is double the other, they keep them. If not, they are turned face down again. At the end, they check each pair is correct using the 5p coins.

N33 Addition/subtraction

ACTIVITY 1
Whole class, in pairs

• *Subtracting two 2-digit numbers with a difference of between 1 and 9*
Number cards (1 to 9) (PCM 2)
Each pair draws three circles on their paper and writes a 1-digit number in each. Write a subtraction on the board, e.g. '42 – 39 ='. Each pair calculates the answer, counting on from the smaller number up to the nearest ten (40) and using one finger for each number spoken. *How many fingers are you holding up*? Then counting on to the larger number. *How many fingers in total*? If the number of fingers matches a circle number, they may cross out that circle. Write another subtraction on the board and repeat. The first pair to cross out all three circles can shout *Bingo!*

ACTIVITY 2
3 children

• *Subtracting by counting on from the smallest number*
Number cards (30 to 40 and 41 to 50) (PCMs 4, 5), card for labels ('–', '='), post-it notes
Shuffle each set of cards and put them in a pile face down. Take a card from each pile and make a subtraction using the '–' card. Count up from the smaller to the larger number and record the answer on a post-it. Place the '=' card and the post-it beside the subtraction. Repeat with another two cards.

ACTIVITY 3
3 children

• *Subtracting by counting on (up to 10)*
• *Recognising the difference between two numbers*
Two sets of number cards (1 to 9) (PCM 2), blank number track (numbered 1 to 10) (PCM 1), post-it notes
Shuffle the cards and place them in a pile face down. One child turns over a card and reads the number. The second child turns over another card and the children lay these cards side by side. The third child finds the smaller number on the number track. The first child counts along from that number to the second number. They write the difference on a post-it note and stick it between the two cards. They repeat, swapping roles.

ACTIVITY 4
3 children

• *Recognising pairs of 2-digit numbers with a difference of 11 or 9*
Number grids (1 to 100) (PCM 19)
How many pairs of numbers can the children find on the grid which have a difference of 11? How many pairs with a difference of 9? Join the different pairs. Can they find a pattern? Repeat for other differences: 5, 12, 24...

ACTIVITY 1
Whole class, in pairs

- *Recognising the place-value of digits in a 3-digit number*
Place-value cards (hundreds, tens, units) (PCMs 10 to 12)
Shuffle the cards and place them in a pile face down. Each pair draws five circles on paper and writes a 3-digit number in each. Take a card from each pile and read out the number. E.g. you take a 6, a 30 and a 200 and make 236. Does any pair have a number in one of their circles which begins with the same hundreds digit? If so, they can cross out that circle. Continue playing like this until one pair has crossed out all their circles.

ACTIVITY 2
3 children

- *Recognising the place-value of digits in a 3-digit number*
- *Recognising the multiples of ten in 3-digit numbers*
- *Counting in ones from a 3-digit number*
Place-value cards (hundreds, tens and units) (PCMs 10 to 12), interlocking cubes
Shuffle the cards and place them face down in a pile on the table. One child takes a units card. He lays it on the table face up. The second child takes a tens card and places it under the units card to make a 2-digit number. The third child takes a hundreds card and places it under the tens and units cards to make a 3-digit number. All the children read the number in turn. They count on in ones from that number. Each time they say a new number, they take a cube if they are correct. When they reach a multiple of ten, they stop. They repeat the activity, each taking another card and making a new 3-digit number.

ACTIVITY 3
3 children

- *Recognising the numbers before and after a 3-digit number*
A book with over 500 pages
The first child chooses a 3-digit number, e.g. 187. The second child writes down the number that comes before it, i.e. 186, without consulting the book. The third child uses the book to check the answer. The first child writes down the number that comes after it, i.e. 188, and the second child checks the answer with the help of the book. The children continue, sharing roles.

ACTIVITY 4
3-4 children

- *Recognising the place-value of digits in a 3-digit number*
Five sets of number cards (0 to 9) (PCM 2), a three-column table (headed 'H', 'T' and 'U'), interlocking cubes
Shuffle the cards and place them face down in a pile. The children take turns to pick three cards and place them in any of the columns. Once placed, a card cannot be moved. They record their numbers and the child with the largest 3-digit number wins that round and takes a cube. The children play five rounds. Who has the most cubes? Extend the activity by letting the child with the smallest number win.

ACTIVITY 5
2-3 children

- *Recognising 'largest' and 'smallest' in a set of 3-digit numbers*
- *Reasoning about number and organising ideas*
Number cards (0 to 9) (PCM 2)
Using the cards, which is the largest 3-digit number the children can make? Which is the smallest? Ask them to write them down. The children place number card 4 in the hundreds' position. Using each of the other cards once only in each number, how many numbers can they make? Now ask them to place number card 0 in the tens' position. Using each of the other cards once only in each number, how many numbers can they make?

N35 Doubling/halving

ACTIVITY 1
Whole class, in pairs

- *Doubling a number (1 to 10)*
Number cards (1 to 10) (PCM 2), interlocking cubes, counters
Shuffle the cards and place them in a pile face down. Select a card and ask a pair to say double the number. If they are correct, they collect a counter. Ask the class to check each pair's doubling, using the cubes to help if necessary. Who collects the most counters?

ACTIVITY 2
2-3 children

- *Halving an even number, up to 20*
Number cards (2, 4, 6 ... 20) (PCMs 2, 3), interlocking cubes, 1p coins
Shuffle the cards, and place them in a pile face down. The children take turns to select a card, and say what half of the number is. If they are correct, they collect a matching number of 1p coins. Ask the children to check each other's halving, using the cubes to help if necessary. Who collects the most money?

ACTIVITY 3
3-4 children

- *Halving an even number, up to 100*
- *Collecting coins in 10p and 1p coins, exchanging ten 1p coins for a 10p coin, when necessary*
Infant game 18: 'Snake tables', a dice, counters, coins (1p, 10p)
The children each place a counter at 'start'. They take turns to roll the dice and move their counter a matching number of spaces. If their counter lands on a number in a yellow space, they halve the number and collect 10p and 1p coins to match the number of the half. Ask the children to check each other's calculations. When one player reaches the end of the snake, the game is over. Who collects the most money? Remind the children that they can change sets of 1p coins for 10p coins.

ACTIVITY 4
2-3 children

- *Doubling 2-digit amounts of money in 10p and 1p coins*
Coins (1p, 10p), a feely bag
The children place some of the coins in the bag, and leave some out. They take turns to take a handful of coins from the bag, e.g. 34p, and then say double the amount. Suggest that they build another pile of 34p from the coins outside the bag to help calculate the double. Ask the children to record the result, i.e. 'double 34p = 68p'.

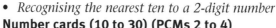

ACTIVITY 1
Whole class, in pairs

- *Recognising the nearest ten to a 2-digit number*
Number cards (10 to 30) (PCMs 2 to 4)
The cards are shuffled, and placed in a pile, face down. Reveal a card, and read it. Choose a pair to say its nearest multiple of ten. The other pairs check the answer. Repeat for each pair. Repeat with cards 40 to 60.

ACTIVITY 2
3-4 children

- *Recognising the nearest ten to a 2-digit number*
Number cards (1 to 100) (PCMs 2 to 8), two sets of tens cards (10, 20 ... 100) (PCM 9)
Spread out the number cards and the tens cards (in order) separately, face up, on the table. The children select two number cards 'nearest to' each tens card, e.g. number cards 43 and 41 can be paired with tens card 40. They place the pair on top of the tens card. Extend the activity by asking the children to choose a number card which is less than its nearest tens card and one which is more than its nearest tens card, e.g. for 40 they can choose 38 and 44.

ACTIVITY 3
2-3 children

- *Recognising the nearest ten to a 2-digit number*
Number grid 4 (PCM 16 – enlarged to A3), two sets of tens cards (10, 20 ... 100) (PCM 9)
The children cover each number on the grid with its nearest tens card. For example, space 41 will be covered by card 40. Is there a number which is not covered by a card?

ACTIVITY 4
4 children

- *Recognising the nearest ten to a 2-digit number*
Number cards (5 to 100) (PCMs 2 to 8), tens cards (10, 20 ... 100) (PCM 9)
Deal ten number cards to each child. Shuffle the tens cards and place them face down in a pile. Reveal the first tens card. The children lay down any card which has that tens card as its nearest ten. Continue until all the tens cards have been turned over. The winner is the first child to lay down all his/her cards.

N37 Addition/subtraction

ACTIVITY 1
Whole class, in pairs

- *Creating additions or subtractions using two numbers*
- *Relating simple additions or subtractions to real life situations*

Number cards (1 to 20) (PCMs 2, 3), strips of paper

Shuffle the cards and place them in a pile face down. The children each take two cards, e.g. 3 and 15. They must arrange these two numbers to make an addition or subtraction and write it on their strip of paper. Choose a pair to show the class their strip. Write their calculation on the board, e.g. '3 + 12 = 15'. Can they make up a story which involves having to add three and twelve? E.g. *I have 3p and my mum gives me 12p more. How much do I have now?* Continue around the class, looking at the calculations and hearing the number stories.

ACTIVITY 2
2 pairs

- *Reasoning about numbers*
- *Relating addition and subtraction*

Number cards (1 to 20) (PCMs 2,3)

The children draw a number machine with an 'IN' and an 'OUT'. Pairs take turns to place one of the cards at the IN and one at the OUT. The other pair have to guess what the machine is doing to the number (e.g. adding 3, subtracting 4 etc.). Both pairs write the matching calculation, replace the cards and repeat.

ACTIVITY 3
3-4 children

- *Adding amounts of money (up to 60p)*
- *Comparing amounts of money to find 'largest' and 'smallest'*

Interlocking cubes in different colours, cubes price list (red = 2p, blue =5p, green = 1p, other = 10p), coins (1p, 2p, 5p, 10p, 20p)

The children make a tower using six cubes. They work out how much their tower is worth, using the price list above. They check the value of each other's towers, using coins to help them.

ACTIVITY 4
3 children

- *Reasoning with number and organising ideas*
- *Creating simple additions and subtractions*

Interlocking cubes

Using 1-digit numbers, each child writes a simple addition or subtraction on a piece of paper and hides it from the others. They take turns to reveal two of the numbers in their calculation, e.g. 3 and 4. The others have to try to guess the third number, e.g. 7 (3 + 4 = 7). If they are right first time, they take two cubes. If not, they can guess again, e.g. 1 (4 – 3 = 1). If they are right this time, they may take one cube. If not, the child must reveal his calculation. The children continue until someone has ten cubes.

N38 Addition

ACTIVITY 1
Whole class, in pairs

- *Doubling numbers (up to 15)*
- *Recognising even numbers (up to 30)*

Number cards (1 to 15) (PCMs 2, 3), interlocking cubes

Each pair gives you a target number (an even number between 2 and 30). Write them on the board with their initials alongside. Shuffle the cards and place them in a pile face down. Turn over a card and say the number. Each pair doubles this number and writes down the answer. If the number is their target number, they take a cube. Repeat with different target numbers.

ACTIVITY 2
3 children

- *Doubling numbers (up to 15)*
- *Recognising doubles of numbers (up to 15)*

Number cards (1 to 15) (PCMs 2, 3), coins (1p, 2p, 5p, 10p, 20p,50p, £1), counters

Shuffle the number cards and place them in a pile face down. One child turns over a card and hides it from the others. They double the card number and lay out the answer in coins. The others have to guess what the number is on the card. If they guess correctly, they take a counter. The children repeat the activity several times, taking turns to reveal the card. Who has collected the most counters?

ACTIVITY 3
3 children

- *Doubling numbers (up to 9)*
- *Recognising near double additions (totalling up to 20)*

Number cards (0 to 9) (PCM 2), interlocking cubes

Shuffle the cards and place them in a pile face down. One child turns over a card and takes that number of cubes. The second child has to take a matching number of cubes. The third child writes down the addition, e.g. '5 + 5 = 10'. The first child now writes a near doubling addition beneath it, e.g. '5 + 6 = 11'. The others check, using the cubes. They repeat, swapping roles.

ACTIVITY 4
3 children

- *Doubling numbers and amounts of coins (up to 100/£1)*
- *Matching coins to written numbers*

Fives cards (5, 10, 15 ... 100) (PCMs 2 to 8), coins (5p), post-it notes

Spread the cards out face down on the table. One child takes a card, e.g. 15. The second child takes this amount in coins, e.g. three 5p coins. The third child has to take the same number of coins again. The children work out the double of this number, write it on a post-it note and stick it on the card. They repeat, swapping roles.

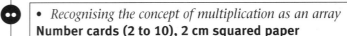 **N39** **Multiplication**

ACTIVITY 1
Whole class, in pairs

- *Recognising the concept of multiplication as an array*
Number cards (2 to 10), 2 cm squared paper
Select a card at random and write the number on the board. Each pair draws a grid on squared paper with a matching number of squares. They write a multiplication to match. Choose different pairs to discuss their grids and record some on the board. Repeat.

ACTIVITY 2
3-4 children

- *Recognising the concept of multiplication as an array*
Number cards (1 to 5) (PCM 2), counters
Shuffle the cards and place them face down on the table. The children reveal a card and match the number with rows of two counters, e.g. for card 3, they make three rows of two counters. Ask them to say how many counters there are altogether, in terms of the rows, e.g. *Three rows of twos are six*. The children repeat the process for each card. Extend the activity by asking the children to make rows of three counters.

ACTIVITY 3
3-4 children

- *Recognising the concept of multiplication as an array*
- *Recording multiplication using '×' notation*
2cm squared paper, rulers
The children draw rectangles using the lines on the squared paper. Within the rectangles, they count the number of rows and the number of squares in each row. They record their counting and write the corresponding multiplication, e.g. '4 × 2 = 8'.

ACTIVITY 4
3-4 children

- *Recognising the concept of multiplication as an array*
- *Recognising multiplication using '×' notation*
Pegs, peg-board
The children make different arrangements of two rows of pegs. They record each arrangement as a multiplication in the ×2 table, e.g. '7 × 2 = 14'. Extend the activity by asking the children to make arrangements of three rows of pegs, and then four rows of pegs.

ACTIVITY 5
3-4 children

- *Recognising the concept of multiplication as an array*
- *Recording multiplication using '×' notation*
- *Recognising the commutative property of multiplication*
Squared paper, pencils, rulers, scissors, large sheet of paper, glue
The children draw a rectangle on the squared paper and cut it out. They cut out another identical rectangle. They stick the two rectangles on a sheet of paper, so that they illustrate two multiplications, e.g. 3 × 5 = 15 and 5 × 3 = 15.
Let them repeat the activity for different sized pairs of identical rectangles.

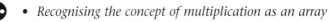

ACTIVITY 1
Whole class

- *Recognising division as the grouping of objects*
- *Recording the grouping using '÷' notation*

Interlocking cubes
Starting with 12 cubes, ask the children to group them in twos, counting how many groups are created. They record the division, i.e. '12 ÷ 2 = 6'. Ask them to repeat the activity, grouping the 12 cubes in threes, fours, and sixes. Extend the activity by asking the children to do the same with 24 cubes.

ACTIVITY 2
3-4 children

- *Recognising division as the grouping of objects*
- *Recording the grouping using '÷' notation*

Counters
The children make piles of two counters. Starting with two piles of two counters, they count the total number of counters, and write down the corresponding division, i.e. '4 ÷ 2 = 2'. They make three piles of two counters, and so on, recording the division each time. Extend the activity by asking the children to make piles of three counters. (Some children may need to record by drawing the counters rather than using the '÷' notation.)

ACTIVITY 3
3-4 children

- *Recognising the concept of division using an array*
- *Recording the division using ÷ notation*

Squared paper, rulers
The children draw rectangles using the lines on the squared paper. They count the total number of squares inside the rectangle. They count the number of rows and the number of squares in each row. Finally, they record their counting and write the corresponding division, e.g. '20 ÷ 4 = 5'.

ACTIVITY 4
3-4 children

- *Recognising division as the grouping of objects*
- *Recording the grouping using ÷ notation*
- *Recognising the concept of a remainder*

1p coins
The children start with a handful of 1p coins, e.g. 21. They explore grouping them in twos, counting the number of groups, and any remainders, and write a corresponding division, i.e. '21 ÷ 2 = 10 remainder 1'. They then explore grouping the 21 coins in other ways, writing the division each time. Extend the activity by letting the children start with a different number of coins.

ACTIVITY 1
Whole class, in pairs

• *Dividing quantities into halves and quarters*
Interlocking cubes, plastic cups
Each pair scoops up a cupful of cubes. They tip them out and count them. If the number can be halved exactly, they score two points. If the number can be quartered exactly, they score four points. They write down the number and fraction, and replace the cubes. The winner is the first pair to reach 20 points. Check the winning pair's answers with the class.

ACTIVITY 2
3-4 children

• *Dividing quantities into halves and quarters*
• *Recognising patterns of numbers on a number line which can be halved and can be quartered*
Number cards (1 to 20) (PCMs 2, 3), interlocking cubes
The children make a line of all the numbers from 1 to 20 that can be halved exactly. They can use the cubes to help them. When they have done this, they make a line of all numbers from 1 to 20 that can be quartered exactly.

ACTIVITY 3
3-4 children

• *Dividing quantities of pennies into halves and quarters*
• *Recording fractions of amounts using fraction notation*
1p coins
The children take a large handful of coins and count how many they have. They share the coins between two children to see if the amount can be halved. If so, they record the result, e.g. '$\frac{1}{2}$ of 12p = 6p'. They try to divide the same amount into quarters, recording the fraction each time. If it cannot be divided, they make a note of the number and take another handful. Repeat with different handfuls of coins.

ACTIVITY 4
2-3 children

• *Recognising numbers which can be divided into halves, thirds and quarters*
Number grid 4 (PCM 16), interlocking cubes (blue, yellow and red), coins (1p, 10p)
The children place a red cube on all the numbers in the grid that can be halved exactly. They place a blue cube on all the numbers that can be quartered exactly. They place a yellow cube on all the numbers that can be divided into thirds. They can use the coins to help them.

ACTIVITY 5
Pair

• *Matching fractions of shapes to the correct fraction notation*
Concept keyboard with a word processor (create overlay and file to match)
The children take turns to match the teddies to the houses to which they belong. E.g. Anna belongs to the $\frac{1}{3}$ family. Their partner decides whether they are correct.

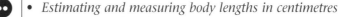

ACTIVITY 1
Whole class, in pairs

- *Estimating and measuring body lengths in centimetres*
- *Measuring, indirectly, round or curved lengths*

10-centimetre strips, scissors, paper

The children make strips of paper in the following lengths:
– the circumference of their wrist;
– the circumference of their ankle;
– the circumference of their leg, just above the knee.
They lay out the strips of paper and write an estimate of the length of each one in centimetres. They measure the lengths of the strips with the 10-centimetre strips and write the measurements on the strips.

ACTIVITY 2
2-3 children

- *Estimating and measuring lengths of objects in centimetres*

10-centimetre strips of paper, a collection of classroom objects

The children write down the name of each object. They estimate the length of each in centimetres, and write their estimate alongside the name. They use the measuring strips to measure the actual length of each object, checking that all members of the group agree with the measurements. They write the measured lengths alongside the estimates. Ask them to discuss how good each estimate is.

ACTIVITY 3
3-4 children

- *Collecting centicubes in tens and units*
- *Recognising lengths of more than 10 centimetres as tens and unit centimetres*

A dice, 10-centimetre strips, centicubes

The children take turns to throw the dice. They take a matching number of centicubes and place them in a line. When they have ten cubes they exchange them for a 10-centimetre strip. The winner is the first child to collect three strips.

ACTIVITY 4
Pairs

- *Measuring heights in centimetres*

10-centimetre strips

Working together with the 10-centimetre strips, the children measure each other's height in centimetres. They carefully draw a picture of themselves and write their height alongside the picture.

M2 **Length**

ACTIVITY 1
Whole class, in groups of 3

- *Estimating and measuring lengths of objects in centimetres*
10-centimetre strips of paper, a collection of classroom objects
Give each group some objects to measure in centimetres. They draw the object, e.g. a pencil, and estimate its length in centimetres. They check the actual length with the 10-centimetre strip and label each drawing. Compare the estimates. Who was closest?

ACTIVITY 2
3 children

- *Collecting centicubes in tens and units*
- *Recognising lengths of more than 10 centimetres as tens and unit centimetres*
- *Recognising that there are 100 cm in one metre*
Number cards (1 to 20) (PCMs 2, 3), 10 10-centimetre strips of paper, centicubes
Shuffle the cards and place them face down in a pile. The children take turns to pick a card and take a matching number of centimetres. E.g. the first child picks 13 and takes one 10-centimetre strip and three centicubes. The card is returned to the bottom of the pile. Each time a child collects ten centicubes they exchange them for a 10-centimetre strip. The winner is the first child to reach one metre, i.e. ten 10-centimetre strips.

ACTIVITY 3
3-4 children

- *Estimating and measuring lengths in metres and centimetres*
- *Recognising objects which are about one metre long*
Metre sticks (marked in cms)
The children look for objects or lengths in the room which are close to one metre long. They write down the name of each object. Using the metre sticks, they measure them exactly in centimetres, and record the lengths alongside the names. How close can they get to an exact length of one metre?

ACTIVITY 4
4-5 children

- *Estimating lengths in metres*
- *Measuring lengths in metres and centimetres*
Metre sticks (marked in cms)
The children take turns to estimate the length of a room or a corridor. They write down all their estimates and use the metre sticks to check the actual length. How long is it in metres and centimetres? How close were the children's estimates?

M3 Time

ACTIVITY 1
Whole class, in groups of 3-4

• *Showing the hour and half hour times on an analogue clock*
Clock-face sheet (PCM 28), scissors
The children draw hands on the clock faces to show different o'clock and half past times. They cut them out and put them in order. Check each 'time line' with the rest of the class.

ACTIVITY 2
2 pairs

• *Showing and reading the hour and half hour times on analogue and digital clocks*
An analogue clock with moveable hands, digital clock-face sheet (PCM 29)
One pair sets a half past time on the clock, the other pair must write the time on a digital clock on their sheet. Each pair must check that both clocks match, then they reverse roles. The children continue the activity until the whole sheet has been filled in.

ACTIVITY 3
3-4 children

• *Showing and reading the hour and half hour times on analogue and digital clocks*
Clock-face sheet (PCM 28), digital clock-face sheet (PCM 29), scissors
The children choose a half past time, e.g. half past four. They draw that time by putting hands on one of the blank analogue clock faces and also by writing in the numbers on one of the digital clocks. They cut out both clock faces and put them together. The children continue, choosing different half past times, until both clock-face sheets have been filled in.

ACTIVITY 4
5-6 children

• *Showing and reading the hour and half hour times on analogue and digital clocks*
Number cards (1 to 12) (PCMs 2, 3), an analogue clock with moveable hands, digital clock-face sheet (PCM 29), interlocking cubes
Shuffle the cards and place them face down in a pile. On the blank sheet, all the children except one, who is the caller, write down four digital times, all at half past the hour. The caller takes the top card, reads the number and sets the clock to show half past that hour. He shows it to the other children. If a child has a matching time on one of her digital clock faces, she covers it with a cube. The caller continues turning over cards and setting the clock. The winner is the first player to cover all four of their clock faces.

ACTIVITY 5
Pair

• *Matching written times, analogue times and digital times (using o'clock and half past times)*
Concept keyboard with word processor (create an overlay and file to match)
The children take turns to match the time on the left to the correct clock faces. Their partner checks that they are correct.

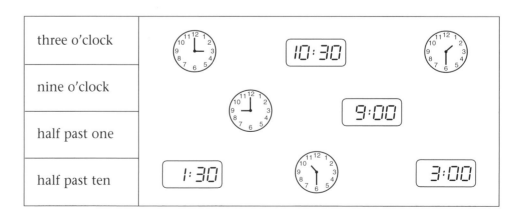

ACTIVITY 1
Whole class, in groups of 3-4

- *Drawing the hands for quarter hour times on an analogue clock face*

Clock-face sheet (PCM 28), scissors

The children draw the hands on the blank clock faces to show different times at quarter past and quarter to the hour. They cut these out and order them. Check each time line with the rest of the class.

ACTIVITY 2
3 children

- *Showing and reading the quarter hour times on an analogue clock*

An analogue clock with moveable hands, a pair of interlocking circles

The first child sets the interlocking circles to represent one of the quarters of the hour. The second child sets the clock at a time which matches the circles. The third child checks that they both match and reads the time on the clock. The children do this several times, sharing the roles.

ACTIVITY 3
2 pairs

- *Showing and reading the quarter hour times on an analogue clock*

An analogue clock with moveable hands, number cards (1 to 12) (PCMs 2, 3)

One pair chooses a card from the pile, e.g. 7. The other pair must set the hands of the clock to show quarter past that hour, i.e. quarter past seven. The children swap roles and continue taking turns until all the cards have been used. Let the children repeat the activity for times at a quarter to the hour.

ACTIVITY 4
3-4 children

- *Showing and reading the quarter hour times on an analogue clock*

An analogue clock with moveable hands, a dice, interlocking cubes

The children start with the clock hands set at midnight. They take turns to throw the dice, move the long, minute hand around the clock a matching number of quarters, then say the time shown on the clock. If a child finishes their turn with the minute hand on the 12, he takes a cube. The children continue until the short, hour hand has moved round the clock twice and the hands are at midnight again.

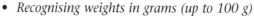**M5** **Weight**

ACTIVITY 1
Whole class, in pairs

- *Ordering written standard weights*
- *Recognising weights in grams (up to 100 g)*

A collection of food labels

The children study the labels. What are the weights on the labels? Ask them to put the labels in order from the heaviest to lightest. Which pairs are correct? Discuss the correct order with the class.

ACTIVITY 2
3+ children

- *Estimating weights of objects*
- *Matching objects to standard weights (up to 100 g)*

A balance, weights (1 g, 10 g, 100 g), a collection of objects

Can the children find anything that weighs exactly 100 g, 10 g, etc?

ACTIVITY 3
3 children

- *Recognising and estimating 1 kg*

A balance, 1 kg weight, sticky tape or string, a collection of objects

The children find three objects which, together, weigh 1 kg. To make weighing the objects easier, suggest that they tape or tie the three objects together.

ACTIVITY 4
3 children

- *Recognising and estimating 100 g and 1 kg*

A balance, weights (100 g, 1 kg), wooden bricks

The children estimate how many bricks will weigh 100 g. They weigh some bricks using the balance, and compare the number with their estimate.
Ask them to repeat the activity with the kilogram weight. Are there enough bricks to check the weight? If not, can they predict how many will weigh 1kg?

Capacity

ACTIVITY 1
3 children

- *Recognising the standard units of capacity (one litre)*
- *Ordering containers by capacity using standard measures*

A collection of containers (with about 1 litre capacity), a litre measure, water

The children sort the containers into two groups: those with a capacity of less than a litre, and those with a capacity of more than a litre. They do this by filling each with water and then pouring the water into the litre measure to check.

ACTIVITY 2
3 children

- *Using different non-standard measures*
- *Estimating the capacity of a container*

A large jug, a collection of non-standard measures (e.g. margarine tub, beaker, yoghurt pot), water

The children measure the capacity of the water jug using, in turn, a different non-standard measure. Before each measuring they write an estimate of how many of the measures they think will be required.

ACTIVITY 3
3 children

- *Recognising the standard unit of capacity (one litre)*
- *Using non-standard measures to fill a one litre container*
- *Estimating the capacity of a container in non-standard units*

A collection of small containers (e.g. margarine tub, eggcup, beaker), a litre measure, water

Using one container at a time, the children investigate how many times they have to fill the container with liquid to fill the litre measure. Each child must first of all estimate the outcome. They fill each container with water and pour the water into the litre measure, keeping count of how many times the container has to be filled. Extend the activity by asking the children to investigate how many times each container has to be filled to reach half a litre.

ACTIVITY 4
2+ children

- *Recognising the standard units of capacity (one litre)*
- *Carrying out an investigation using a one litre measure*

A litre measure, a cup, a beaker, water

The children investigate how many litres of liquid they each drink in a week. They should first make an estimate, and then use the beaker and cup to investigate their consumption.

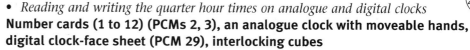

M7 Time

ACTIVITY 1
Whole class, in pairs

• *Reading and writing the quarter hour times on analogue and digital clocks*
Number cards (1 to 12) (PCMs 2, 3), an analogue clock with moveable hands, digital clock-face sheet (PCM 29), interlocking cubes
Shuffle the cards and place them face down in a pile. Each pair writes down four digital times (all quarter past or quarter to the hour) on their clock-face sheet. Take the top card, read the number and set the clock to show either quarter past or quarter to the hour of that number. If a pair has a matching digital display, they cover it with a cube. Continue turning over cards and setting the clock. The winner is the first pair to cover three of their four clock faces.

ACTIVITY 2
2 pairs

• *Showing, reading and writing the quarter hour times on analogue and digital clocks*
An analogue clock with moveable hands, digital clock-face sheet (PCM 29)
One pair sets a 'quarter past' time on the clock. The other pair must write the time on a digital clock on their sheet. The children should check that they match and then reverse the roles. Let them continue until the whole sheet has been filled in. Extend the activity by asking them to set 'quarter to' times.

ACTIVITY 3
3 children

• *Showing the quarter hour times on an analogue clock and a digital clock*
An analogue clock with moveable hands, digital clock-face sheet (PCM 29), interlocking cubes
The first child writes a 'quarter past' time on one of the digital clock faces. The second child sets the clock hands to match. The third child says what time it will be one hour later. If all three are correct, they each take a cube. Let the children repeat the activity several times, with the children swapping the tasks. Extend the activity by asking them to do the same with 'half past' and 'quarter to' times.

ACTIVITY 4
3-4 children

• *Showing, reading and writing the quarter hour times on analogue and digital clocks*
Clock-face sheet (PCM 28), digital clock-face sheet (PCM 29), scissors, a large sheet of paper, glue
The children choose a quarter past time, e.g. quarter past ten. On the analogue clock-face sheet, they draw the hands to show quarter past ten and write numbers to show the same digital time on the digital clock-face sheet. They do this several times and then repeat the activity for different quarter to times. They cut out both sets of clocks and put them together. They display them on a large sheet of paper.

ACTIVITY 5
Pair

• *Matching written times, analogue times and digital times (using quarter-past and quarter to times)*
Concept keyboard with word processor (create overlay and file to match)
The first child presses a written time on the left, their partner presses the correct clock face. Repeat, swapping roles.

quarter to 5	
quarter past 2	
quarter past 8	
quarter to 1	

Capacity

ACTIVITY 1
3-4 children

- *Calibrating a container to be used for measuring capacity*
- *Measuring the capacity of containers using a non-standard measure*

A cylindrical container, rubber bands, a cup, a collection of containers, water
The children calibrate the cylindrical container by pouring in cupfuls of water and fitting rubber bands around the outside of the container to record the level after each cup. They then use the container to measure the capacity of some other containers in terms of cupfuls.

ACTIVITY 2
3-4 children

- *Calibrating a container to be used for measuring capacity*
- *Measuring the capacity of containers using a non-standard measure*

A cylindrical container, rubber bands, yoghurt pots, a collection of containers, water
The children calibrate the cylindrical container by pouring in yoghurt pots of water and fitting rubber bands around the outside of the container to record the levels after two potfuls at a time. They then use the container to find the capacity of some other containers in terms of yoghurt pots, e.g. 2 rubber bands is '4 potfuls'. Point out to the children that they will need to approximate capacities which measure levels between the rubber bands.

ACTIVITY 3
3 children

- *Calibrating a container to be used for measuring capacity*
- *Measuring the capacity of containers using a non-standard measure*

A small bottle, rubber bands, eggcups, water, a collection of containers
The children calibrate the bottle by pouring eggcups of water (five at a time) into the bottle. After each five pourings, they put a rubber band around the outside of the bottle to mark the water levels. They then use the bottle to find the capacity of some other containers in terms of eggcups, e.g. 3 rubber bands is 15 eggcupfuls

ACTIVITY 4
3 children

- *Calibrating a container to be used for measuring capacity*
- *Measuring the capacity of containers using a non-standard measure*

Calibrated cylindrical containers (in cupfuls and potfuls), a collection of containers, water
The children measure the capacity of each container using the calibrated measures and record the results.

ACTIVITY 5
3 children

- *Using a one litre measure*
- *Measuring the capacity of containers (up to one litre)*

A litre measure, a collection of containers, water
The children measure the capacity of each container using the calibrated litre measure and record the results in ml.

49

M9 **Time**

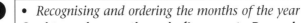

ACTIVITY 1
Whole class, in pairs

- *Recognising and ordering the months of the year*

Card to make month cards (January to December)

The children spread out the month cards randomly in a straight line. They put them in order, from January to December, then say the months, in sequence. Repeat, taking turns to swap any two months in one go. Ask them to count how many swaps are needed to put them in order.

ACTIVITY 2
3-4 children

- *Recognising and ordering the months of the year*
- *Recognising the month which comes after, and those which come before a given month*

Card to make two sets of month cards (January to December), interlocking cubes

The children spread out one set of month cards, in order, in a straight line. They shuffle the other set and place them in a pile face down. They take turns to reveal a card, and say the month **after** the month on the card. They must try to do it without looking at the line of cards. All the children look at the line to check. If correct, a cube is collected. Let them continue until they have all had four turns. Repeat, this time stating the month **before** the month on the card. Who collects the most cubes?

ACTIVITY 3
4 children

- *Recognising and ordering the months of the year*
- *Recognising the month which comes after, and those which come before a given month*

Card to make two sets of month cards (January to December), interlocking cubes

The children lay out the cards from one set, in order, from January to December. Shuffle the other set of cards and deal three to each child. The children take turns to play a card. The first child must put down either May, June or July. The second child then puts down the month which comes just before or just after that month, and so on. For example, if the first child puts down July, the second may put down June or August. If at any time a child cannot play, he must take a cube. The children continue taking turns to place a month or take a cube. When all the months are laid out, the winner is the child with the fewest cubes.

ACTIVITY 4
3 children

- *Recognising the four seasons of the year*
- *Recognising the months which belong to each season of the year*

Card to make two sets of month cards (January to December)

Decide with the children which months fall into each of the four seasons. Shuffle the cards and deal three to each child. Place the remainder face down in a pile, and place the top card face up next to it. Each child chooses to collect a season. Taking turns, the children may choose either the top card of the face down pile or the top card of the face up pile. They may then keep this month and discard one from their hand, or discard the month they have just selected. The discarded months are placed on the face up pile. The winner is the first child to collect a season of three months.

ACTIVITY 1
Whole class, then in groups of 3-4 children

- *Beginning to recognise the number of minutes in one hour*
- *Counting minutes in fives*

An analogue clock with moveable hands, a dice, interlocking cubes

Start with the clock hands set at midday. Choose children to throw the dice and move the minute hand around the clock a matching number of five minutes. E.g. the first child throws 3, he moves the hands around the clock 15 minutes. If, during their turn, the minute hand passes 12, the child collects a number of cubes, indicated by the hour hand. The children continue until the hour hand is back at 12. The winner is the child with the fewest cubes.

ACTIVITY 2
3-4 children

- *Estimating one minute, and different numbers of seconds*
- *Recognising the number of seconds in one minute*

A stop clock with a second hand

The children take turns to estimate the length of a minute. One child acts as timer, while another child attempts to estimate one minute. The timer keeps the clock face away from the estimator, starts the clock as he begins to count, then stops it on command. The timer then shows the estimator the clock to reveal how close the estimate is. Extend the activity by asking the children to estimate 30 seconds or 45 seconds.

ACTIVITY 3
4 children

- *Recognising the number of hours in a day*

Day cards (Monday to Sunday) (PCM 30), a dice, interlocking cubes

Spread out the cards face up on the table. The children take turns to throw the dice and collect a matching number of cubes. Each cube represents one hour. When a child has collected 24 hours, they choose a day card. The winner is the first child to collect two days.

ACTIVITY 4
Pairs

- *Calculating periods of time in minutes*
- *Recognising the number of minutes in one hour*

A calculator

The children calculate how many minutes have passed between two different times, e.g. from 12 o'clock to 9 o'clock. Can they estimate how many minutes they have been in school today? Help by suggesting times if some find this difficult. Ask them to record each result. Extend the activity by asking them to calculate how many minutes must pass before particular times are reached.

M11 Time

ACTIVITY 1
3-4 children

- *Beginning to recognise the number of hours in one day*
- *Reading o'clock times*

An analogue clock with moveable hands, a dice, interlocking cubes

The children start with the clock hands set at midday. They take turns to throw the dice and move the hour hand around the clock a matching number of hours. E.g. if the first child throws 3, he moves the hands around three hours, and says the time. The children should check each other's turns.

ACTIVITY 2
3-4 children

- *Recognising the number of days in one week*

Four sets of day cards (Monday to Sunday) (PCM 30), a dice, a counter, interlocking cubes

The children arrange the cards in lines, one week per line, from Monday to Sunday. They place the counter on the first Monday. They take turns to throw the dice and move the counter along the cards a matching number of days. E.g. if the first child throws 2, he moves the counter to Wednesday, and says the day. If, on their next turn, they move to the beginning of the next week, they collect cubes to match the number of the week, i.e. in moving from the third to the fourth week, they collect three cubes. The winner is the first to get to the end of four weeks. (Develop the game by making rules e.g. land on Sunday, miss a go.)

ACTIVITY 3
Pairs

- *Recognising and counting periods of time in weeks*

A calculator

The children work out how many weeks have passed since particular times, e.g. since the beginning of term. They then work out how many weeks there are to go until particular times. They record their findings on paper.

ACTIVITY 4
Pairs

- *Recognising the number of hours in different periods of time*

A calculator

The children calculate how many hours there are in different periods of time, e.g. in one week, two weeks, three days, etc.

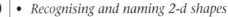 **S1** **3-d shape**

ACTIVITY 1
Whole class, then in groups of
3-4 children

- *Recognising and naming 2-d shapes*
- *Naming and describing a face of a 3-d shape*

A set of 3-d shapes with flat faces (cubes, cuboids, pyramids, prisms), a feely bag

Place the shapes in the bag. The children take turns to pick any shape from the bag and describe one or more of its faces. The others have to check that the description is correct.

ACTIVITY 2
3-4 children

- *Naming and describing a face of a 3-d shape*

A set of 3-d shapes (cubes, cuboids, pyramids, spheres, cones, cylinders), shape labels (cone, cylinder, cube, cuboid, pyramid, sphere, others) (PCM 24)

Spread out the labels on the table and place the shapes in the bag. The children take turns to pick a shape from the bag and place it beside its label.

ACTIVITY 3
4 children

- *Naming and describing a face of a 3-d shape*

A set of 3-d shapes with flat faces (cubes, cuboids, pyramids, prisms), a feely bag

Place the shapes in the bag. The children take turns to feel for a shape, describe the shape of one of its faces, e.g. *It has a square face*, then remove it to check. If they are correct, they keep it. Otherwise, they replace it in the bag. The children continue until all the shapes have been removed.

ACTIVITY 4
2-5 children

- *Recognising and naming common 3-d shapes*

A set of 3-d shapes (cubes, cuboids, pyramids, spheres, cones, cylinders), a book or a board

The children use the book or board as a wall. They take turns to be in charge of the shapes, revealing them very slowly from behind the wall. The others have to name the shape as soon as they can. If they are correct, they keep the shape.

ACTIVITY 5
3 children

- *Sorting 3-d shapes according to the shape of their faces*
- *Naming and describing a face of a 3-d shape*

A set of 3-d shapes with flat faces (cubes, cuboids, pyramids, prisms), shape labels (square face, rectangle face, triangle face, pentagon face, hexagon face) (PCM 25), two hoops, a feely bag

Lay the hoops on the table so that they intersect. Choose a label to put on each hoop. Place the shapes in the bag. The children take turns to pick a shape from the bag and place it in the correct position inside or outside the hoops. Let the children repeat the activity with a different pair of labels.

S2 Angle

ACTIVITY 1
Whole class, then 2+ children

- *Recognising clockwise and anticlockwise turns*

The children work out how many clockwise and anticlockwise turns are needed to move from one place to another, e.g. from the desk to the sink, desk to the door, classroom to the hall. They record their findings, describing each turn and the total number of turns.

ACTIVITY 2
3 children

- *Recognising clockwise and anticlockwise turns*
- *Using a programmable toy to follow a route*

Roamer or floor turtle, chalk

The children devise a six-stage route from A to B using clockwise and anticlockwise turns. They program the roamer to follow the route, marking A and B on the floor. The children then describe the route from B to A, and program the roamer to follow this route.

ACTIVITY 3
2 children

- *Recognising clockwise and anticlockwise turns*

Game 23: 'Clockwise', a dice, counters

(See instructions on the card.)

ACTIVITY 4
2+ children

- *Recognising clockwise and anticlockwise turns*
- *Constructing a maze and a route using right-angle turns*

Squared paper, rulers

The children use squared paper to design a maze. They start by drawing a square outline (the outside of the maze) with several gaps or entry points. They draw the route from the outside to the centre of the maze, using right-angled turns. Finally, they draw the hedges or fences in position. They redraw the maze on a different sheet of paper with the hedges and fences but without the route to the centre. They challenge the others in the group to find the route. When all the group has tried to solve each other's routes, each child then describes their own solution, using clockwise and anticlockwise turns.

ACTIVITY 5
2+ children

- *Recognising clockwise and anticlockwise turns*
- *Interpreting a street map or plan*

Local street plan or school plan

The children mark a route from home to school on the street plan, or from classroom to classroom on the school plan. They describe the journey using clockwise and anticlockwise turns.

ACTIVITY 1
Whole class

• *Recognising and naming 2-d shapes*
Sets of 2-d shapes
The children sit in a circle, holding one shape each. Ask them to stand up if they are holding a pentagon. Let them check each other's shapes. The children sit down. Repeat, asking for different shapes. After a few goes, ask the children to pass their shape to the child on their left. Start again.

ACTIVITY 2
2 children

• *Recognising and naming 2-d shapes*
• *Reading the names of 2-d shapes*
Infant game 24: 'Shape match', a dice, counters, shape labels (square, rectangle, circle, pentagon, hexagon, triangle, octagon, others) (PCM 23)
Place the shape labels face down on the table. The children take turns to reveal a label, then place a counter (one colour per child), if possible, on a matching shape on the board. When all of the shapes are covered by counters, who has covered the most?

ACTIVITY 3
3-4 children

• *Recognising and naming 2-d shapes*
• *Reading the names of 2-d shapes*
Plastic shapes (squares, rectangles, triangles, circles, pentagons, hexagons, octagons), shape labels (square, rectangle, pentagon, hexagon, octagon, triangle, circle, others) (PCM 23), a feely bag
Spread out the labels on the table, and place the shapes in the bag. The children take turns to pick a shape from the bag and place it beside its label.

ACTIVITY 4
7 children

• *Recognising and naming 2-d shapes*
Three sets of shape cards (PCMs 21, 22)
Shuffle the cards and deal them out. Each child chooses to collect either squares, circles, rectangles, triangles, pentagons, hexagons or octagons. The children take turns to swap a card with another child. The winner is the first to have three cards of their chosen shape.

ACTIVITY 5
3-4 children

• *Recognising and naming 2-d shapes*
Shape cards (PCMs 21, 22)
Spread out the cards face down on the table. The children take turns to reveal two cards. If the shapes have the same name, they keep them and take another turn. Otherwise, the cards are turned back over. The children continue until all the cards have been collected. The winner is the child who has collected the most cards.

S4 # 2-d shape

ACTIVITY 1
3 children

- *Recognising the number of corners in 2-d shapes*
- *Naming common 2-d shapes*

A set of 2-d shapes (squares, rectangles, triangles, circles, pentagons, hexagons), a dice

Spread out the shapes on the table. The children take turns to throw the dice and collect a shape with a matching number of corners. If there are no corresponding shapes, they miss a turn. They try to name the shape. The winner is the first child to collect five shapes.

ACTIVITY 2
2 children

- *Recognising the number of sides in 2-d shapes*

Game 24: 'Shape match', dice, counters

(See instructions on the card.)

ACTIVITY 3
3-4 children

- *Recognising the number of sides in 2-d shapes*
- *Naming common 2-d shapes*

Number cards (1 to 6) (PCM 2), shape cards (PCMs 21, 22)

Spread out the number cards on the table. Shuffle the shape cards and place them face down in a pile. The children take turns to reveal the top card, count the number of sides and then place it beside a matching number card. They try to name the shape.

ACTIVITY 4
3 children

- *Recognising the number of corners in 2-d shapes*
- *Naming common 2-d shapes*

A set of 2-d shapes, a feely bag, counters

Place the shapes in the bag. The children take turns to feel for a shape, then take it out of the bag, counting its corners. They pick up a matching number of counters and then name the shape, playing four rounds in total. The winner is the child who has collected the fewest counters. Repeat, this time the winner is the child with the most counters.

ACTIVITY 5
3+ children

- *Drawing a 2-d shape with a given number of sides*

A dice

One child rolls the dice, then each child draws a shape with a matching number of sides. They check each other's drawings then play again with a different child rolling the dice. Can they name any of the shapes?

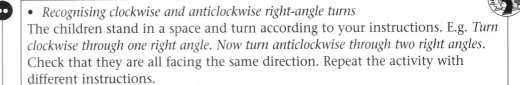

S5 Angle

ACTIVITY 1
Whole class

• *Recognising clockwise and anticlockwise right-angle turns*
The children stand in a space and turn according to your instructions. E.g. *Turn clockwise through one right angle. Now turn anticlockwise through two right angles.* Check that they are all facing the same direction. Repeat the activity with different instructions.

ACTIVITY 2
2+ children

• *Recognising right-angles in 2-d shapes*
Right angle measures, a set of 2-d shapes
Using the right-angle measure, the children test for a right angle in each shape. They sort them into two groups, those which have a right angle and those which don't. They record the results by drawing the shapes on two separate sheets of paper.

ACTIVITY 3
2 children

• *Recognising clockwise and anticlockwise right-angle turns*
The children investigate journeys for which only right-angle turns are allowed. They count how many right-angle turns are needed to move from, e.g. the desk to the door, the classroom to the staffroom door, the hall to the playground. They should record the turns. Which are clockwise and which are anticlockwise?

ACTIVITY 4
2+ children

• *Recognising angles which are more, less or equal to a right angle*
Right-angle measures, crayons, scissors
Using the right-angle measure, the children draw and cut out some angles which are less than a right angle and colour them green. They do the same for some angles which are more than a right angle and equal to a right angle, colouring them red and blue respectively. Make a display of the angles, grouping them together.

ACTIVITY 5
2+ children

• *Drawing a 2-d shape with a given number of right angles*
Right-angle measures, rulers, scissors
With the help of the right-angle measures, the children draw shapes with one right angle only. Then they draw shapes with only two right angles, then only three right angles etc. Ask the children to cut out the shapes and display them.

ACTIVITY 6
2+ children

• *Recognising right-angle turns*
• *Interpreting a street map or plan*
Local street plan or school plan
The children devise a journey on the street plan from home to school, or on the school plan from one classroom to another. They draw an outline of the journey on the plan, and count how many right-angle turns they need.
As an extension to the activity, ask them to investigate different journeys for which only four right-angle turns are allowed.

S6 **Symmetry**

ACTIVITY 1
Whole class, in pairs

- *Recognising a line of symmetry*
- *Completing a symmetrical drawing, given one 'half' of the drawing*

Mirrors, paper, rulers

Each child draws a fold line on a sheet of paper with a ruler. They draw half a shape on one side of the fold line. They swap pictures and try to complete the symmetrical shape. The children can use the mirror to help them complete the shape, and also to test for the accuracy of the final drawing.

ACTIVITY 2
2+ children

- *Recognising a line of symmetry*
- *Creating a symmetrical shape*

Mirrors, paper, scissors

The children fold a sheet of paper in half and cut out a piece, using two straight line cuts about the fold line. They then open the cut-out symmetrical piece and place a mirror on the fold line, checking the reflection.

ACTIVITY 3
2+ children

- *Recognising a line of symmetry*
- *Creating a symmetrical pattern*

Scissors

The children create symmetrical patterns. They take a sheet of paper, fold it in half, and then open it out. They draw a shape or pattern on one side of the fold line. Making sure that the shape is visible through the paper, they fold the paper shut (alternatively, fold it back the other way), cut around the outline of the shape, and then open it out to reveal a symmetrical shape. Let the children experiment with different symmetrical shapes and patterns.

ACTIVITY 4
2+ children

- *Beginning to recognise lines of symmetry in common 2-d shapes*

A set of 2-d shapes, scissors

The children use the shapes as templates. They draw around each one on a sheet of paper and cut out the shapes. They then investigate for lines of symmetry by folding the paper shapes. They draw any lines of symmetry on the shapes with a ruler. Make a display of the shapes with their names.

ACTIVITY 5
Pair

- *Recognising and creating symmetrical patterns*

KidPix software (or similar drawing software package)

The children take turns to use the wacky paintbrush and the symmetry option to create their own symmetrical pictures. They print it out and colour it in using crayons/pencils/pens. They fold each other's pictures to check, or use a mirror.

ACTIVITY 6
Pairs

- *Recognising a line of symmetry*
- *Creating a symmetrical pattern*

A4 paper, coloured sticky shapes (self-adhesive)

Each child folds their paper in half. They unfold it and create a pattern against the fold line using the sticky shapes. They swap papers and finish each other's shapes on the other side of the fold line, to create a symmetrical pattern.

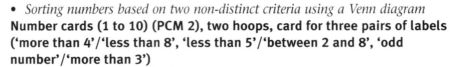

D1 Sorting

ACTIVITY 1
3-4 children

• *Sorting objects based on two non-distinct criteria using a Venn diagram*
Playing cards, two hoops, card for four pairs of labels ('black'/'picture card', 'red'/'less than 6', 'heart'/'red', '5 or more'/'8 or less')
Place the hoops on the table so that they intersect. The children take one pair of labels and place one on each hoop. They then sort the cards, placing them inside or outside the hoops, according to the labels. They use each pair of labels and repeat the activity.

ACTIVITY 2
3-4 children

• *Sorting numbers based on two non-distinct criteria using a Venn diagram*
Number cards (1 to 10) (PCM 2), two hoops, card for three pairs of labels ('more than 4'/'less than 8', 'less than 5'/'between 2 and 8', 'odd number'/'more than 3')
Place the hoops on the table so that they intersect. Taking one pair of labels, the children place one on each hoop. The children then sort the cards, placing them inside or outside the hoops, according to the labels. They repeat the activity with the other pairs of labels.

ACTIVITY 3
3-4 children

• *Sorting objects based on two non-distinct criteria using a Venn diagram*
A set of dominoes, two hoops, card for three pairs of labels ('more than 6 spots'/'less than 9 spots', 'less than 7 spots'/'between 3 and 9 spots', 'total is even'/'less than 7 spots')
Place the hoops on the table so that they intersect. The children take a pair of labels and place one on each hoop. They then sort the dominoes, placing them inside or outside the hoops, according to the labels. They use the other pairs of labels and repeat the activity.

ACTIVITY 4
3-4 children

• *Sorting 2-d shapes based on two non-distinct criteria using a Venn diagram*
2-d shapes in different colours, two hoops, blank cards, crayons
Using the blank cards, the children make different colour labels and different shape labels. Place the hoops on the table so that they intersect. The children then select one of each label and place them on the hoops. They sort the 2-d shapes and put them inside or outside the hoops, according to the labels. They repeat the activity for a different choice of labels. What happens if they choose two colour labels or two shape labels?

 Sorting

D2

ACTIVITY 1
4-5 children

• *Sorting objects based on two non-distinct criteria using a Carroll diagram*
A set of dominoes, large 2 x 2 Carroll diagram (PCM 27 — enlarged to A3)
The children sort the dominoes using a Carroll diagram, according to the following criteria: total number of spots is even/total number of spots is odd (columns); total number of spots is less than 7/total number of spots is not less than 7 (rows). How many dominoes are in each category? Repeat the activity for a different total number of spots.

ACTIVITY 2
4-5 children

• *Sorting numbers based on two non-distinct criteria using a Carroll diagram*
Number cards (1 to 50) (PCMs 2 to 5), large 2 x 2 Carroll diagram
(PCM 27 — enlarged to A3)
The children sort the cards using a Carroll diagram, according to the following criteria: even number/odd number (columns); in the fives/not in the fives (rows). How many cards are in each category? When you have checked their work, ask the children to sort the cards in a different way, for you to guess the criteria.

ACTIVITY 3
4-5 children

• *Sorting objects based on two non-distinct criteria using a Carroll diagram*
Playing cards (aces to 9s), large 2 x 2 Carroll diagram
(PCM 27 — enlarged to A3)
The children deal out ten cards. They sort them using a Carroll diagram according to the following criteria: red/black (columns); more than 5 /not more than 5 (rows). How many cards are in each category? The children experiment with different ways of sorting them.

ACTIVITY 4
4 children

• *Sorting objects based on two non-distinct criteria using a Carroll diagram*
• *Constructing 3-d models using a fixed number of interlocking cubes*
Interlocking cubes (blue and green), large 2 x 2 Carroll diagram
(PCM 27 — enlarged to A3)
The children build models with five cubes. All the models must be different. How many different models can they make using only five cubes? They sort the models using a Carroll diagram according to the following criteria: less than four cubes in a line /not less than four cubes in a line (columns); contains a blue or a green cube/does not contain a blue or green cube (rows). How many models are in each category? When you have checked their work, let the children sort the cubes in a different way, for you to guess the criteria.

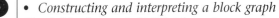 **Block graphs**

ACTIVITY 1
Whole class, then groups of 4

• *Constructing and interpreting a block graph*

Blank block graph (PCM 26, or 2 cm squared paper), felt-tipped pens

Head the graph 'pet ownership', with the axes labelled: 'number of children' (vertical), and 'pets' (horizontal). The columns should be labelled along the horizontal axis: 'dog', 'cat', 'fish', 'bird', 'hamster' etc. Conduct a class survey, completing the graph appropriately. Some children will appear in more than one column if, e.g. they have a fish and a cat. Which column has the most blocks? What is the most commonly owned pet? In groups, the children construct their own graphs on different criteria.

ACTIVITY 2
4-5 children

 • *Constructing and interpreting a block graph*

2 cm squared paper, two dice, felt-tipped pens

Ask the children to draw a graph 'Throwing two dice' and to label the vertical axis 'number' and the horizontal axis 'dice total' (from 1 to 12). The children take turns to throw the two dice and add the numbers, e.g. 4 + 2. They colour a block on the graph above the appropriate number, i.e. 6. They should do this at least 30 times. What is the shape of the completed graph?

ACTIVITY 3
4-5 children

• *Constructing and interpreting a block graph*

Blank block graph (PCM 26, or 2 cm squared paper), interlocking cubes (about 30 using five colours), a feely bag, crayons

Ask the children to head the graph 'cube colours' and label the vertical axis 'number' and the horizontal axis 'colour'. Label the columns along the horizontal axis to match the five colours of the interlocking cubes, e.g. 'red', 'blue', 'green', 'yellow' and 'pink'. The children place all the cubes in the bag and take out one each, colouring a block to match the colour of the cube. Let them continue until all the cubes are used. How many of each colour have been drawn from the bag?

ACTIVITY 4
4-5 children

• *Constructing and interpreting a block graph*

Blank block graph (PCM 26, or 2 cm squared paper), two dice, felt-tipped pens

Ask the children to head the graph 'Throwing two dice' and label the vertical axis 'number' and the horizontal axis 'dice difference' (numbered 0 to 5). The children throw the two dice, e.g. 5 and 2, and find the difference between the numbers, i.e. 3. They colour a block on the graph above the number 3. They should do this at least 40 times. What do they notice?

ACTIVITY 5
Pair

 • *Collecting information to create a block graph*

Appropriate spreadsheet software or graphing package

The children collect information about pet ownership in the class, using the information gathered in Activity 1 and enter the information into a simple graphing package or a spreadsheet previously set up by the teacher to generate a block graph.

D4 **Sorting**

ACTIVITY 1
3-4 children

• *Sorting numbers using a Venn diagram for two non-distinct criteria*
A set of dominoes, two hoops, card for three pairs of labels ('more than 5 spots'/'less than 8 spots', 'less than 5 spots'/'between 4 and 9 spots', 'more than 6 spots'/'total is odd')
Place the hoops on the table so that they intersect. The children take one pair of labels and place one label on each hoop. They sort the dominoes, placing them inside or outside the hoops, according to the labels. They repeat the activity with another pair of labels.

ACTIVITY 2
3-4 children

• *Sorting numbers using a Venn diagram for two non-distinct criteria*
Playing cards, two hoops, four pairs of labels ('red'/'more than 4', 'black'/'more than 5', 'even'/'red', '4 or more'/'7 or less')
Place the hoops on the table so that they intersect. The children take one pair of labels and place one on each hoop. They sort the cards, placing them inside or outside the hoops, according to the labels. They repeat the activity with a different pair of labels.

ACTIVITY 3
3-4 children

• *Deducing the properties of two sets of numbers, given the numbers in their position in the Venn diagram*
Number cards (1 to 20) (PCMs 2, 3), two hoops, blank cards
Using the blank cards, the children make labels to sort the number cards. The labels could say, for example, 'even', 'odd', 'two digits', 'more than 7' etc. Place the hoops on the table so that they intersect. The children choose two labels as criteria for sorting the cards inside or outside the hoops. However, they do not place the labels on the hoops. The labels are turned face down for you to guess the criteria. They repeat the activity by sorting the cards in different ways.

ACTIVITY 4
2-3 children

• *Sorting numbers using a Venn diagram for two non-distinct criteria*
Number cards (1 to 50) (PCMs 2 to 5), two hoops, three labels ('both digits odd', 'both digits even', 'one odd, one even digit'), two labels ('digit total less than 6', 'digit total more than 9')
Place the hoops on the table so that they intersect. The children place one of each type of label on the hoops. They choose 20 of the number cards and place them inside or outside the hoops, according to the labels. They repeat the activity for a different pair of labels.

D5 Tables

ACTIVITY 1
Whole class, in groups of 5-6

• *Creating and interpreting a table of information*
Blank tables (five columns) (one per group)
The children write column headings on the table: 'name', 'more than 4 letters', 'less than 7 letters', 'has an 'e'', 'has an 'a''. They write each other's names in the first column, then complete the table with ticks and crosses, according to each individual name. They discuss the information in the table, e.g. how many ticks and crosses there are in each column and what this means. Put the whole class's results together, and discuss.

ACTIVITY 2
3-4 children

• *Creating and interpreting a table of information*
Playing cards, blank table (six columns)
The children write column headings on the table: 'card', 'red', 'black', 'picture card', 'even', 'odd'. They shuffle the cards and put them face down in a pile. They take turns to reveal the top card and write it in the 'card' column, e.g. '4 of H'. They then complete the row with ticks and crosses, according to the description of the card. The children continue until all the cards have been turned over. Discuss the information on the table.

ACTIVITY 3
3-4 children

• *Creating and interpreting a table of information*
A set of dominoes, blank table (four columns)
The children write column headings on the table: 'domino', 'more than 5 spots', 'less than 9 spots', 'odd spots'. They spread out the dominoes, face down. The children take turns to turn over a domino and draw it in the 'domino' column, then complete the row with ticks and crosses, according to how many spots the domino has. They continue until all the dominoes have been turned over. Discuss the information on the table.

ACTIVITY 4
2-3 children

• *Creating and interpreting a table of information*
Number cards (1 to 20) (PCMs 2, 3), blank table
The children create their own table of information about numbers. They start by labelling the first column 'number', then choose their own labels about numbers for the other columns, e.g. 'odd', 'even'. They shuffle the cards and choose them randomly, one at a time, writing the number in the first column, then marking ticks and crosses across the column, according to the number chosen. Discuss the information in the table.

Glue here for 0 to 10 track	Photocopy twice and glue here for 0 to 20 track

0	1	2
3	4	5
6	7	8
9	10	

15	20
14	19
13	18
12	17
11	16

21	**22**	**23**	**24**
25	**26**	**27**	**28**
29	**30**	**31**	**32**
33	**34**	**35**	**36**

37	38	39	40
41	42	43	44
45	46	47	48
49	50	51	52

53	54	55	56
57	58	59	60
<u>6l</u>	62	63	64
65	<u>66</u>	67	<u>68</u>

<u>69</u>	70	71	72
73	74	75	76
77	78	79	80
<u>81</u>	82	83	84

85	**8̲6̲**	**87**	**88**
8̲9̲	**90**	**9̲1̲**	**92**
93	**94**	**95**	**9̲6̲**
97	**9̲8̲**	**9̲9̲**	**100**

| 10 | 20 | 30 | 40 | 50 |
| 60 | 70 | 80 | 90 | 100 |

1	5 0 0
2	4 0 0
3	3 0 0
4	2 0 0
5	1 0 0

6	0 0 b
7	0 0 8
8	0 0 7
q	0 0 9

1 0	
2 0	0 b
3 0	0 8
4 0	0 ℓ
5 0	0 9

8	I	q	5
6	7	0	8
4	2	6	4
5	q	3	7

4	0	8	6
5	8	9	1
2	4	2	6
3	0	9	7

17	19	13	14
12	15	18	16
17	20	14	13
18	15	16	19

17	44	52	24
71	93	32	61
23	41	82	34
81	62	73	54

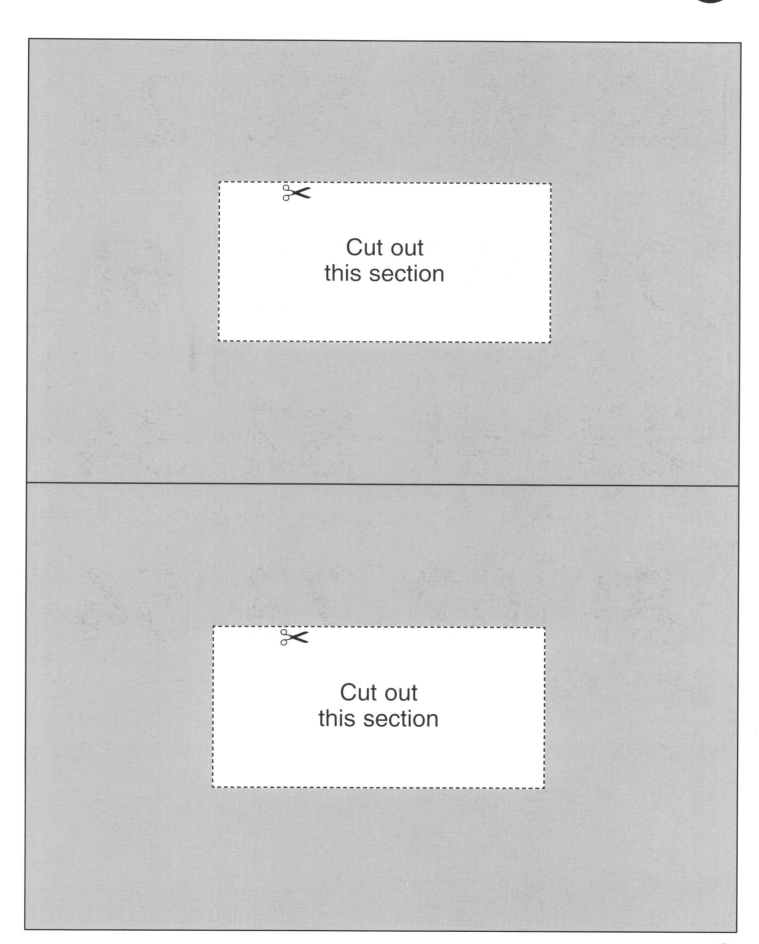

2

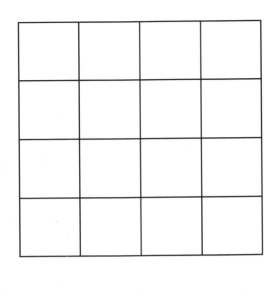

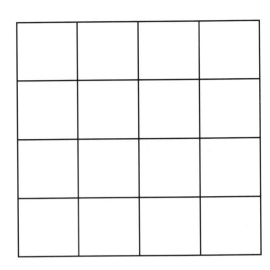

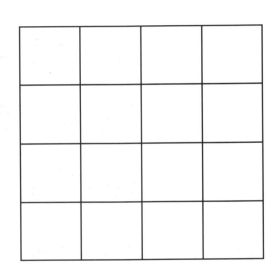

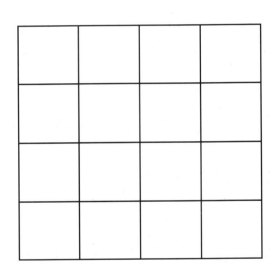

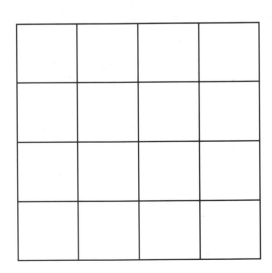

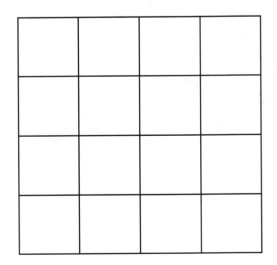

Activity Book PCM 18

1	2	3	4	5	6	7	8	9	10
11	12	13	14	15	16	17	18	19	20
21	22	23	24	25	26	27	28	29	30
31	32	33	34	35	36	37	38	39	40
41	42	43	44	45	46	47	48	49	50
51	52	53	54	55	56	57	58	59	60
61	62	63	64	65	66	67	68	69	70
71	72	73	74	75	76	77	78	79	80
81	82	83	84	85	86	87	88	89	90
91	92	93	94	95	96	97	98	99	100

0	1	2	3	4	5	6	7	8	9
10	11	12	13	14	15	16	17	18	19
20	21	22	23	24	25	26	27	28	29
30	31	32	33	34	35	36	37	38	39
40	41	42	43	44	45	46	47	48	49
50	51	52	53	54	55	56	57	58	59
60	61	62	63	64	65	66	67	68	69
70	71	72	73	74	75	76	77	78	79
80	81	82	83	84	85	86	87	88	89
90	91	92	93	94	95	96	97	98	99

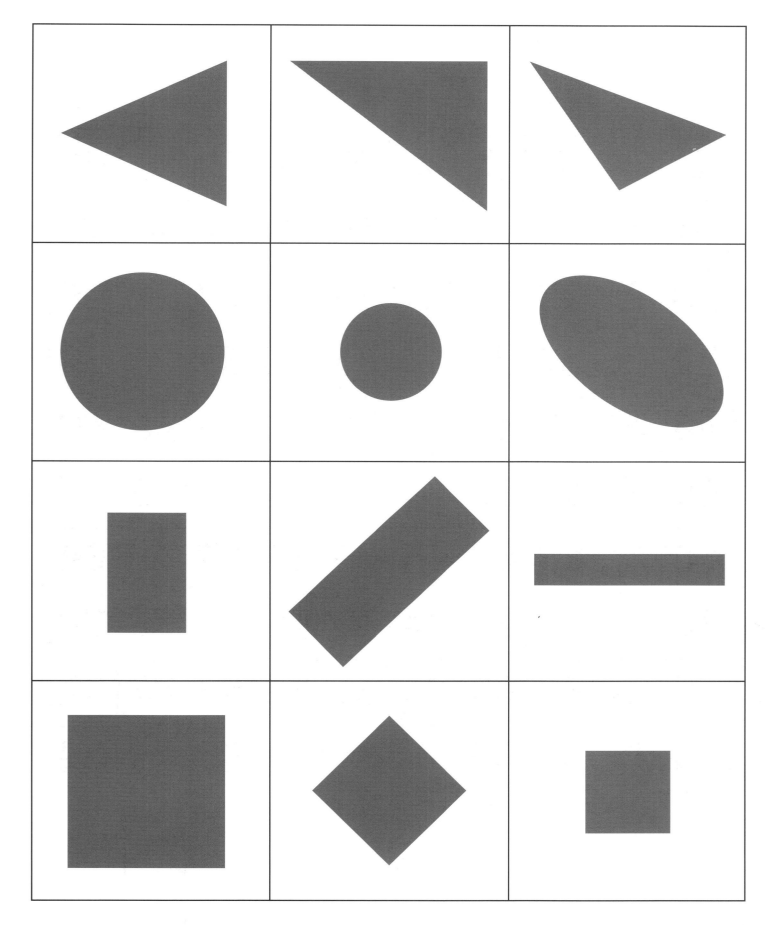

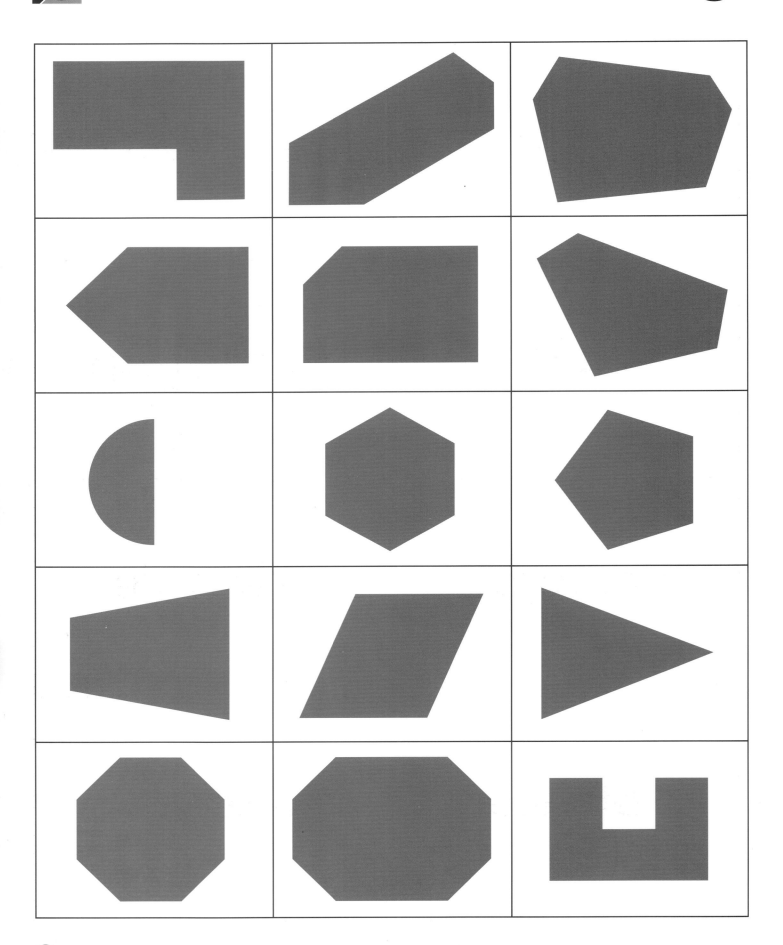

square	**rectangle**
circle	**pentagon**
hexagon	**triangle**
others	**octagon**

cube	cuboid
pyramid	sphere
cone	cylinder
others	

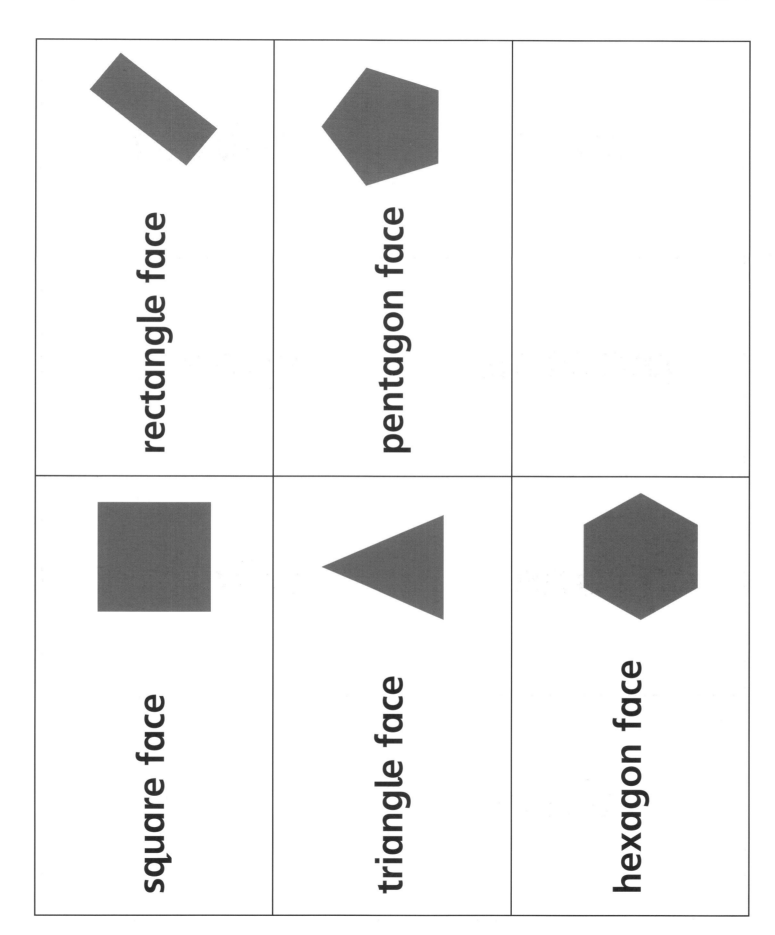

rectangle face

pentagon face

square face

triangle face

hexagon face

title:

10						
9						
8						
7						
6						
5						
4						
3						
2						
1						

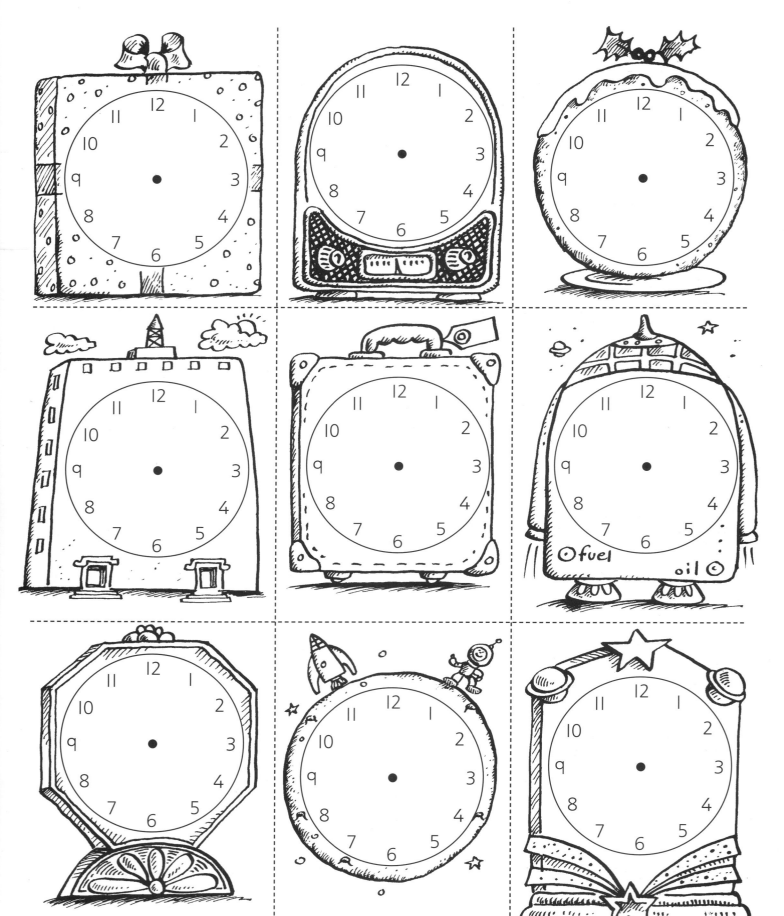

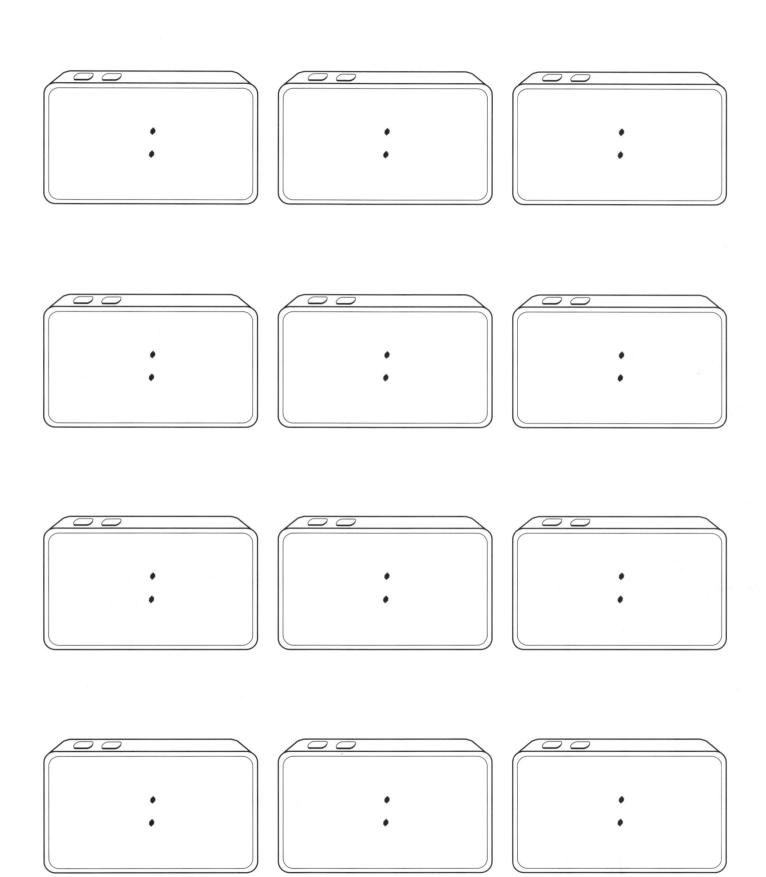

Monday	**Tuesday**
Wednesday	**Thursday**
Friday	**Saturday**
Sunday	